ENGINEERING MECHANICS
STATICS

R. C. HIBBELER

STATICS STUDY PACK

FREE BODY DIAGRAM WORKBOOK
PETER SCHIAVONE

WORKING MODEL SIMULATION CD
JOE GUARINO

PROBLEMS WEBSITE
RUSSELL C. HIBBELER

Prentice
Hall

PRENTICE HALL, Upper Saddle River, NJ 07458

Acquisitions Editor: Eric Svendsen
Supplement Editor: Kristen Blanco
Special Projects Manager: Barbara A. Murray
Production Editor: Barbara A. Till
Supplement Cover Manager: Paul Gourhan
Supplement Cover Designer: PM Workshop Inc.
Manufacturing Buyer: Lisa McDowell

© 2001 by Russell C. Hibbeler
Published by Prentice Hall
Upper Saddle River, NJ 07458

Printed in the United States of America

10 9 8 7 6 5 4 3

ISBN   0-13-029435-7

Prentice-Hall International (UK) Limited, London
Prentice-Hall of Australia Pty. Limited, Sydney
Prentice-Hall Canada, Inc., Toronto
Prentice-Hall Hispanoamericana, S.A., Mexico
Prentice-Hall of India Private Limited, New Delhi
Pearson Education Asia Pte. Ltd., Singapore
Prentice-Hall of Japan, Inc., Tokyo
Editora Prentice-Hall do Brazil, Ltda., Rio de Janeiro

Foreword

The Statics Study Pack was designed to help students improve their study skills. It consists of three study components — a free body diagram workbook, a Visualization CD based on Working Model Software, and an access code to a website with over 1000 sample Statics and Dynamics problems and solutions.

- **Free Body Diagram Workbook** — Prepared by Peter Schiavone of the University of Alberta. This workbook begins with a tutorial on free body diagrams and then includes 50 practice problems of progressing difficulty with complete solutions. Further "strategies and tips" help students understand how to use the diagrams in solving the accompanying problems.

- **Working Model CD** — Prepared with the help of Joe Guarino of Boise St. University. This CD contains 63 pre-set simulations of Statics examples in the text that include questions for further exploration. Simulations are powered by the Working Model Engine and were created with actual artwork from the text to enhance their correlation with the text. Directions for CD installation are on the CD's README file. You need to have the CD in your drive when using the simulations. Please also note the licensing terms for using the CD.

- **Problems Website** — Located at http://www.prenhall.com/hibbeler. This Website contains 1000 sample Statics and Dynamics problems for students to study. Problems are keyed to each chapter of the text and contain complete solutions. All problems are supplemental and do not appear in the Eighth or Ninth Edition. Student passwords are printed on the inside cover of the Free Body Diagram Workbook. To access this site, students should go to http://www.prenhall.com/hibbeler, choose the link for the Problems Website, and follow the on-line directions to register. This site also contains an unprotected section with multiple choice check up questions.

Preface

A thorough understanding of how to draw and use a free-body diagram
is absolutely essential when solving problems in mechanics.

This workbook consists mainly of a collection of problems intended to give the student practice in drawing and using free-body diagrams when solving problems in Statics.

All the problems are presented as tutorial problems with the solution only partially complete. The student is then expected to complete the solution by 'filling in the blanks' in the spaces provided. This gives the student the opportunity to build free-body diagrams in stages and extract the relevant information from them when formulating equilibrium equations. Earlier problems provide students with partially drawn free-body diagrams and lots of hints to complete the solution. Later problems are more advanced and are designed to challenge the student more. The complete solution to each problem can be found at the back of the page. The problems are chosen from two-dimensional theories of particle and rigid body mechanics. Once the ideas and concepts developed in these problems have been understood and practiced, the student will find that they can be extended in a relatively straightforward manner to accommodate the corresponding three-dimensional theories.

The book begins with a brief primer on free-body diagrams: where they fit into the general procedure of solving problems in mechanics and why they are so important. Next follows a few examples to illustrate ideas and then the workbook problems.

For best results, the student should read the primer and then, beginning with the simpler problems, try to complete and understand the solution to each of the subsequent problems. The student should avoid the temptation to immediately look at the completed solution over the page. This solution should be accessed only as a last resort (after the student has struggled to the point of giving up), or to check the student's own solution after the fact. The idea behind this is very simple: we learn most when we *do* the thing we are trying to learn - reading through someone else's solution is not the same as actually working through the problem. In the former, the student gains information, in the latter the student gains knowledge. For example, how many people learn to swim or drive a car by reading an instruction manual?

Consequently, since this book is based on *doing*, the student who persistently solves the problems in this book will ultimately gain a thorough, usable knowledge of how to draw and use free-body diagrams.

P. Schiavone

Contents

1

Basic Concepts in Statics

Statics is a branch of mechanics that deals with the study of bodies that are at rest (if originally at rest) or move with constant velocity (if originally in motion) that is, bodies which are in (static) equilibrium.

In mechanics, real bodies (e.g. planets, cars, planes, tables, crates, etc) are represented or *modeled* using certain idealizations which simplify application of the relevant theory. In this book we refer to only two such models:

- **Particle**. A *particle* has a mass but a size/shape that can be neglected. For example, the size of an aircraft is insignificant when compared to the size of the earth and therefore the aircraft can be modeled as a particle when studying its three-dimensional motion in space.

- **Rigid Body**. A *rigid body* represents the next level of sophistication after the particle. That is, a rigid body is a collection of particles which has a size/shape but this size/shape cannot change. In other words, when a body is modeled as a rigid body, we assume that any deformations (changes in shape) are relatively small and can be neglected. For example, the actual deformations occurring in most structures and machines are relatively small so that the rigid body assumption is suitable in these cases.

1.1 Equilibrium

Equilibrium of a Particle

A particle is in equilibrium provided it is at rest if originally at rest or has a constant velocity if originally in motion. To maintain equilibrium, it is necessary and sufficient to satisfy Newton's first law of motion which requires the resultant force acting on the particle or rigid body to be zero. In other words

$$\sum \mathbf{F} = \mathbf{0} \tag{1.1}$$

where $\sum \mathbf{F}$ is the vector sum of all the external forces acting on the particle.

Successful application of the equations of equilibrium (1.1) requires a complete specification of all the known and unknown external forces ($\sum \mathbf{F}$) that act on the object. The best way to account for these is to draw the object's *free-body diagram*.

Equilibrium of a Rigid Body

A rigid body will be in equilibrium provided the sum of all the external forces acting on the body is equal to zero and the sum of the external moments taken about a point is equal to zero. In other words

$$\sum \mathbf{F} = \mathbf{0} \tag{1.2}$$

$$\sum \mathbf{M}_O = \mathbf{0} \tag{1.3}$$

where $\sum \mathbf{F}$ is the vector sum of all the external forces acting on the rigid body and $\sum \mathbf{M}_O$ is the sum of the external moments about an arbitrary point O.

Successful application of the equations of equilibrium (1.2) and (1.3) requires a complete specification of all the known and unknown external forces ($\sum \mathbf{F}$) and moments ($\sum \mathbf{M}_O$) that act on the object. The best way to account for these is again to draw the object's *free-body diagram*.

2

Free-Body Diagrams: the Basics

2.1 Free-Body Diagram: Particle

The equilibrium equation (1.1) is used to determine unknown forces acting on an object (modeled as a particle) in equilibrium. The first step in doing this is to draw the *free-body diagram* of the object to identify the external forces acting on it. The object's free-body diagram is simply a sketch of the object *freed* from its surroundings showing *all* the (external) forces that *act* on it. The diagram focuses your attention on the object of interest and helps you identify *all* the external forces acting. For example:

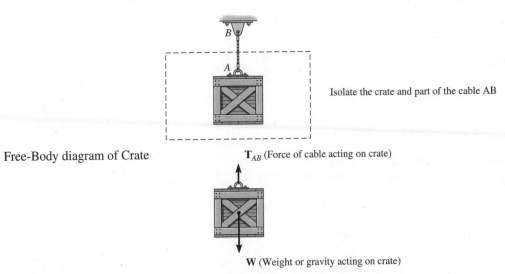

Isolate the crate and part of the cable AB

Free-Body diagram of Crate

$\mathbf{T}_{AB}$ (Force of cable acting on crate)

$\mathbf{W}$ (Weight or gravity acting on crate)

Figure 1

Note that once the crate is *separated* or *freed* from the system, forces which were previously internal to the system become external to the crate. For example, in Figure 1, such a force is the force of the cable *AB acting on the crate*.
Next, we present a formal procedure for drawing free-body diagrams for a particle.

2.1.1 Procedure for Drawing a Free-Body Diagram: Particle

---

1. *Identify the object you wish to isolate.* This choice is often dictated by the particular forces you wish to determine.

2. *Draw the outlined shape of the isolated object.* Imagine the object to be isolated or cut free from the system of which it is a part.

3. *Show all external forces acting on the isolated object.* Indicate on this sketch *all* the external forces that act on the object. These forces can be *active forces*, which tend to set the object in motion, or they can be *reactive forces* which are the result of the constraints or supports that prevent motion. This stage is crucial: it may help to trace around the object's boundary, carefully noting each external force acting on it. Don't forget to include the weight of the object (unless it is being intentionally neglected).

4. *Identify and label each external force acting on the (isolated) object.* The forces that are known should be labeled with their known magnitudes and directions. Use letters to represent the magnitudes and arrows to represent the directions of forces that are unknown.

5. *The direction of a force having an unknown magnitude can be assumed.*

EXAMPLE 2.1

The crate in Figure 2 has a weight of 20lb. Draw free-body diagrams of the crate, the cord BD and the ring at B. Assume that the cords and the ring at B have negligible mass.

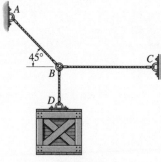

Figure 2

Solution

Free-Body Diagram for the Crate   Imagine the crate to be isolated from its surroundings, then, by inspection, there are only two external forces *acting on the crate*, namely, the weight of 20lb and the force of the cord BD.

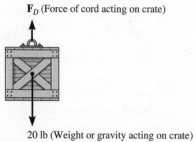

$\mathbf{F}_D$ (Force of cord acting on crate)

20 lb (Weight or gravity acting on crate)

Figure 3

Free-Body Diagram for the Cord BD Imagine the cord to be isolated from its surroundings, then, by inspection, there are only two external forces *acting on the cord*, namely, the force of the crate $\mathbf{F}_D$ and the force $\mathbf{F}_B$ caused by the ring. These forces both tend to pull on the cord so that the cord is in *tension*. Notice that $\mathbf{F}_D$ shown in this free-body diagram (Figure 4) is equal and opposite to that shown in Figure 3 (a consequence of Newton's third law).

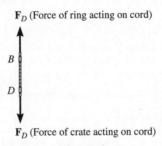

$\mathbf{F}_D$ (Force of ring acting on cord)

$\mathbf{F}_D$ (Force of crate acting on cord)

Figure 4

Free-Body Diagram for the ring at B Imagine the ring to be isolated from its surroundings, then, by inspection, there are actually three external forces acting on the ring, all caused by the attached cords. Notice that $\mathbf{F}_B$ shown in this free-body diagram (Figure 5) is equal and opposite to that shown in Figure 4 (a consequence of Newton's third law).

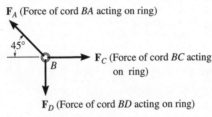

$\mathbf{F}_A$ (Force of cord *BA* acting on ring)

$\mathbf{F}_C$ (Force of cord *BC* acting on ring)

$\mathbf{F}_D$ (Force of cord *BD* acting on ring)

Figure 5

◀

2.1.2 *Using the Free-Body Diagram: Equilibrium*

The free-body diagram is used to identify the unknown forces acting on the particle when applying the equilibrium equation (1.1) to the particle. The procedure for solving equilibrium problems for a particle once the free-body diagram for the particle is established, is therefore as follows:

---

1. *Establish* the x, y-axes in any suitable orientation.
2. Apply the equilibrium equation (1.1) in component form in each direction:

$$\sum F_x = 0 \text{ and } \sum F_y = 0 \qquad (2.1)$$

3. Components are positive if they are directed along a positive axis and negative if they are directed along a negative axis.
4. If more than two unknowns exist and the problem involves a spring, apply $F = ks$ to relate the magnitude of the spring force F to the deformation of the spring s (here, k is the spring constant).
5. If the solution yields a negative result, this indicates the sense of the force is the reverse of that shown/assumed on the free-body diagram.

EXAMPLE 2.2

In Example 2.1, the free-body diagrams established in Figures 3 - 5 give us a 'pictorial representation' of all the information we need to apply the equilibrium equations (2.1) to find the various unknown forces. In fact, taking the positive x-direction to be horizontal ($\rightarrow +$) and the positive y-direction to be vertical ($\uparrow +$), the equilibrium equations (2.1) when applied to each of the objects (regarded as particles) are:

For the Crate: $\uparrow + \sum F_y = 0$: $F_D - 20 = 0$ (See Figure 3)

$$F_D = 20 \text{ lb} \tag{2.2}$$

For the Cord BD: $\uparrow + \sum F_y = 0$: $F_B - F_D = 0$ (See Figure 4)

$$F_B = F_D \tag{2.3}$$

For the Ring: $\uparrow + \sum F_y = 0$: $F_A \sin 45 - F_B = 0$ (See Figure 5)   (2.4)

$\longrightarrow + \sum F_x = 0$: $F_C - F_A \cos 45 = 0$ (See Figure 5)   (2.5)

Equations (2.2)–(2.5) are now 4 equations which can be solved for the 4 unknowns F_A, F_B, F_C and F_D. That is: $F_B = 20$ lb; $F_D = 20$ lb, $F_A = 28.28$, $F_C = 20$. The directions of each of these forces is shown in the free-body diagrams above (Figures 3–5).   ◄

2.2 Free-Body Diagram: Rigid Body

The equilibrium equations (1.2) and (1.3) are used to determine unknown forces and moments acting *on an object* (modeled as a rigid body) in equilibrium. The first step in doing this is again to draw the *free-body diagram* of the object to identify *all of* the external forces and moments acting on it. The procedure for drawing a free-body diagram in this case is much the same as that for a particle with the main exception that now, because the object has 'size/shape,' it can support also external couple moments and moments of external forces.

2.2.1 Procedure for Drawing a Free-Body Diagram: Rigid Body

1. Imagine the body to be isolated or 'cut free' from its constraints and connections and sketch its outlined shape.
2. Identify all the external forces and couple moments that act on the body. Those generally encountered are:
   (a) Applied loadings
   (b) Reactions occurring at the supports or at points of contact with other bodies (See Table 2.1)
   (c) The weight of the body (applied at the body's center of gravity G)
3. The forces and couple moments that are known should be labeled with their proper magnitudes and directions. Letters are used to represent the magnitudes and direction angles of forces and couple moments that are *unknown*. Establish an x, y-coordinate system so that these unknowns e.g. A_x, B_y etc. can be identified. Indicate the dimensions of the body necessary for computing the moments of external forces. In particular, if a force or couple moment has a known line of action but unknown magnitude, the arrowhead which defines the sense of the vector can be assumed. The correctness of the assumed sense will become apparent after solving the equilibrium equations for the unknown magnitude. By definition, the magnitude of a vector is *always positive*, so that if the solution yields a *negative* scalar, the minus *sign* indicates that the vector's sense is *opposite* to that which was originally assumed.

Table 2.1. Supports for Rigid Bodies Subjected to Two-Dimensional Force Systems

	Types of Connection	Reaction	Number of Unknowns
(1)	cable	θ ... F	One unknown. The reaction is a tension force which acts away from the member in the direction of the cable.
(2)	weightless link	θ ... F or θ ... F	One unknown. The reaction is a force which acts along the axis of the link.
(3)	roller	θ ... F	One unknown. The reaction is a force which acts perpendicular to the surface at the point of contact.
(4)	roller or pin in confined smooth slot	F θ or F θ	One unknown. The reaction is a force which acts perpendicular to the slot.
(5)	rocker	θ ... F	One unknown. The reaction is a force which acts perpendicular to the surface at the point of contact.
(6)	smooth contacting surface	θ ... F	One unknown. The reaction is a force which acts perpendicular to the surface at the point of contact.
(7)	member pin connected to collar on smooth rod	θ F or θ F	One unknown. The reaction is a force which acts perpendicular to the rod.
(8)	smooth pin or hinge	F_y θ F_x or F ϕ	Two unknowns. The reactions are two components of force, or the magnitude and direction ϕ of the resultant force. Note that ϕ and θ are not necessarily equal [usually not, unless the rod shown is a link as in (2)].
(9)	member fixed connected to collar on smooth rod	F M	Two unknowns. The reactions are the couple moment and the force which acts perpendicular to the rod.
(10)	fixed support	F_y F_x M or F ϕ M	Three unknowns. The reactions are the couple moment and the two force components, or the couple moment and the magnitude and direction ϕ of the resultant force.

2.2.2 Important Points

- No equilibrium problem should be solved without first drawing the free-body diagram, so as to account for all the external forces and moments that act on the body.
- If a support *prevents translation* of a body in a particular direction, then the support exerts a force on the body in that direction
- If *rotation is prevented* then the support exerts a couple moment on the body
- Internal forces are never shown on the free-body diagram since they occur in equal but opposite collinear pairs and therefore cancel each other out.
- The weight of a body is an external force and its effect is shown as a single resultant force acting through the body's center of gravity G.
- *Couple moments* can be placed anywhere on the free-body diagram since they are *free vectors*. Forces can act at any point along their lines of action since they are *sliding vectors*.

EXAMPLE 2.3

Draw the free-body diagram of the beam, which is pin-connected at A and rocker-supported at B. Neglect the weight of the beam.

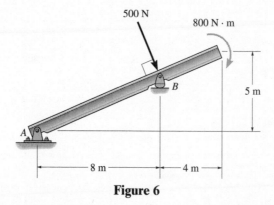

500 N
800 N · m
5 m
B
A
8 m
4 m

Figure 6

Solution

The free-body diagram of the beam is shown in Figure 7. From Table 2.1, since the support at A is a pin-connection, there are two reactions acting on the beam at A denoted by A_x and A_y. In addition, there is one reaction acting on the beam at the rocker support at B. We denote this reaction by the force $\mathbf{F}$ which acts perpendicular to the surface at B, the point of contact (see Table 2.1). The magnitudes of these vectors are unknown and their sense has been assumed (the correctness of the assumed sense will become apparent after solving the equilibrium equations for the unknown magnitude i.e. if application of the equilibrium equations to the beam yields a negative result for $\mathbf{F}$, this indicates the sense of the force is the reverse of that shown/assumed on the free-body diagram). The weight of the beam has been neglected.   ◀

2.2.3 Using the Free-Body Diagram: Equilibrium

The equilibrium equations (1.2) and (1.3) can be written in component form as:

$$\sum F_x = 0, \tag{2.6}$$

$$\sum F_y = 0, \tag{2.7}$$

$$\sum M_O = 0. \tag{2.8}$$

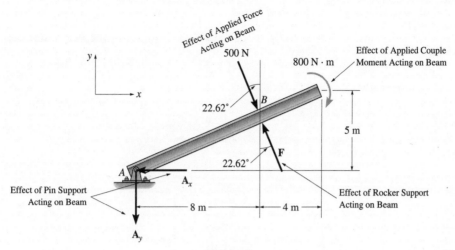

Figure 7

Here, $\sum F_x$ and $\sum F_y$ represent, respectively, the algebraic sums of the x and y components of all the external forces acting on the body and $\sum M_O$ represents the algebraic sum of the couple moments and the moments of all the external force components about an axis perpendicular to the x-y plane and passing through the arbitrary point O, which may lie either on or off the body. The procedure for solving equilibrium problems for a rigid body once the free-body diagram for the body is established, is as follows:

- Apply the moment equation of equilibrium (2.8), about a point (O) that lies at the intersection of the lines of action of two unknown forces. In this way, the moments of these unknowns are zero about O and a direct solution for the third unknown can be determined.
- When applying the force equilibrium equations (2.6) and (2.7), orient the x and y-axes along lines that will provide the simplest resolution of the forces into their x and y components.
- If the solution of the equilibrium equations yields a negative scalar for a force or couple moment magnitude, this indicates that the sense is opposite to that which was assumed on the free-body diagram.

EXAMPLE 2.4

A force of magnitude 150 lb acts on the end of the beam as shown. Find the magnitude and direction of the reaction at pin A and the tension in the cable.

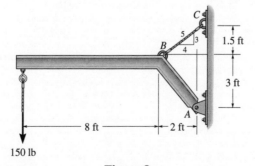

Figure 8

Solution

Free-Body Diagram   The first thing to do is to draw the free-body diagram of the beam in order to identify all the external forces and moments acting on the beam.

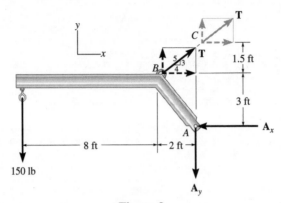

Figure 9

Equations of Equilibrium   The free-body diagram of the beam suggests we can sum moments about the point A to eliminate the moment contribution of the reaction forces $\mathbf{A}_x$ and $\mathbf{A}_y$ acting on the beam. This will allow us to obtain a direct solution for the third unknown i.e. the cable tension T. Taking counterclockwise as positive when computing moments, we have:

$$+ \circlearrowleft \sum M_A = 0: \quad -(3/5)T(2\text{ ft}) - (4/5)T(3\text{ ft}) + 150\text{ lb}(10\text{ ft}) = 0$$
$$-3.6T + 150\text{ lb}(10\text{ ft}) = 0$$
$$T = 416.7\text{ lb} \qquad\qquad\qquad \textbf{Ans.}$$

Summing forces to obtain A_x and A_y, using the result for T, we have

$$\longrightarrow + \sum F_x = 0: \quad -A_x + (4/5)(416.7\text{ lb}) = 0$$
$$\mathbf{A}_x = 333.3\text{ lb} \longleftarrow$$
$$\uparrow + \sum F_y = 0: \quad (3/5)(416.7\text{ lb}) - 150\text{ lb} - A_y = 0$$
$$\mathbf{A}_y = 100\text{ lb} \downarrow$$

Thus, the reaction force $\mathbf{F}_A$ at pin A has magnitude F_A given by:

$$F_A = \sqrt{[(333.3\text{ lb})^2 + (100\text{ lb})^2]} = 348.0\text{ lb}$$

and direction given by

$$\theta = \tan^{-1}[(-100\text{ lb})/(-333.3\text{ lb})] = 196.7°$$

counterclockwise from the positive x-axis or ⟋ 16.7° ◀

3

Problems

3.1 Free-Body Diagrams in Particle Equilibrium

Problem 3.1

The sling is used to support a drum having a weight of 900 lb. Draw a free-body diagram for the knot at A. Take $\theta = 20°$.

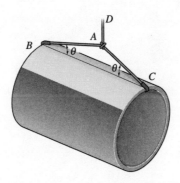

Solution

1. The knot at A has *negligible size* so that it can be modelled as a particle.
2. Imagine the knot at A to be separated or detached from the system.
3. The (detached) knot at A is subjected to three *external* forces. They are caused by:

   i.   **ii.**

   iii.

4. Draw the free-body diagram of the (detached) knot showing all these forces labeled with their magnitudes and directions.

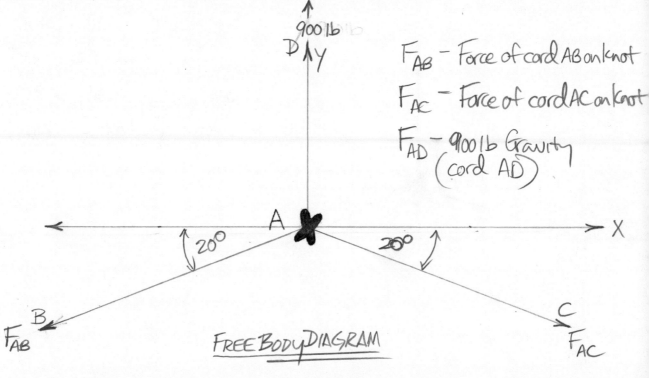

F_{AB} – Force of cord AB on knot

F_{AC} – Force of cord AC on knot

F_{AD} – 900 lb Gravity (cord AD)

FREE BODY DIAGRAM

Problem 3.1

The sling is used to support a drum having a weight of 900 lb. Draw a free-body diagram for the knot at A. Take $\theta = 20°$.

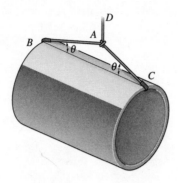

Solution

1. The knot at A has *negligible size* so that it can be modelled as a particle.
2. Imagine the knot at A to be separated or detached from the system.
3. The (detached) knot at A is subjected to three *external* forces. They are caused by:

    i. CORD AB **ii. CORD** AC

   iii. CORD AD *(weight of drum)*

4. Draw the free-body diagram of the (detached) knot showing all these forces labeled with their magnitudes and directions.

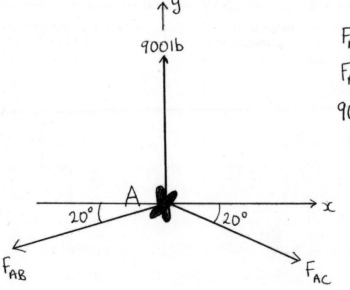

F_{AB} force of cord AB on knot
F_{AC} force of cord AC on knot
900lb force of gravity on knot
(force of cord AD on knot)

Problem 3.2

The spring ABC has a stiffness of 500 N/m and an unstretched length of 6 m. A horizontal force **F** is applied to the cord which is attached to the *small* pulley B so that the displacement of the pulley from the wall is $d = 1.5$ m. Draw a free-body diagram for the small pulley B.

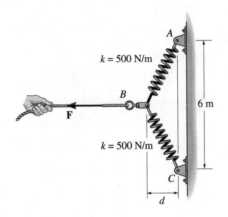

Solution

1. The pulley B has *negligible size* so that it can be modelled as a particle.
2. Imagine the pulley B to be separated or detached from the system.
3. The (detached) pulley B is subjected to three *external* forces. They are caused by:

      i. F_{-x} **ii.** Spring AB

      iii. Spring BC

4. Draw the free-body diagram of the (detached) pulley showing all these forces labeled with their magnitudes and directions. You should also include any other available information e.g. lengths, angles etc. — which will help when formulating the equilibrium equations for the pulley.

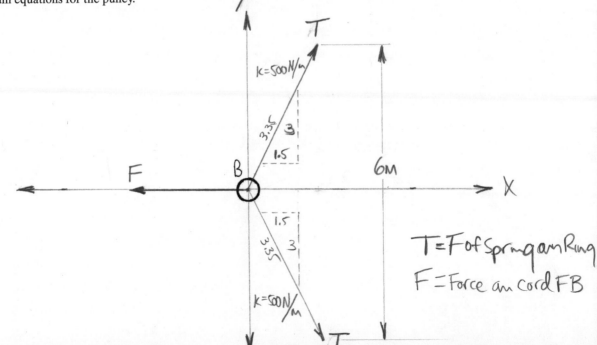

Problem 3.2

The spring ABC has a stiffness of 500 N/m and an unstretched length of 6 m. A horizontal force $\mathbf{F}$ is applied to the cord which is attached to the *small* pulley B so that the displacement of the pulley from the wall is $d = 1.5$ m. Draw a free-body diagram for the small pulley B.

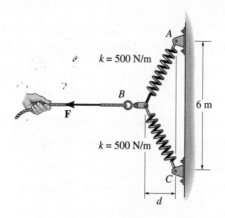

Solution

1. The pulley B has *negligible size* so that it can be modelled as a particle.
2. Imagine the pulley B to be separated or detached from the system.
3. The (detached) pulley B is subjected to three *external* forces. They are caused by:

      i. Force F   **ii. Spring AB**

      iii. Spring BC

4. Draw the free-body diagram of the (detached) pulley showing all these forces labeled with their magnitudes and directions. You should also include any available information e.g. lengths, angles etc. — which will help when formulating the equilibrium equations for the pulley.

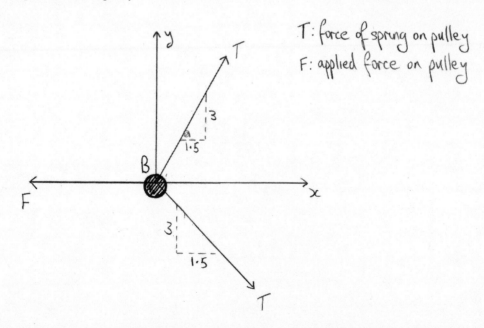

Problem 3.3

The 2-kg block is held in equilibrium by the system of springs. Draw a free-body diagram for the ring at A.

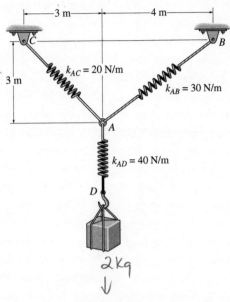

Solution

1. The ring at A has *negligible size* so that it can be modelled as a particle.
2. Imagine the ring at A to be separated or detached from the system.
3. The (detached) ring at A is subjected to three *external* forces. They are caused by:

   i. AD (weight of block)   **ii.** T- AC

   iii. T- AB

4. Draw the free-body diagram of the (detached) ring showing all these forces labeled with their magnitudes and directions. You should also include any other available information e.g. lengths, angles etc. — which will help when formulating the equilibrium equations for the ring.

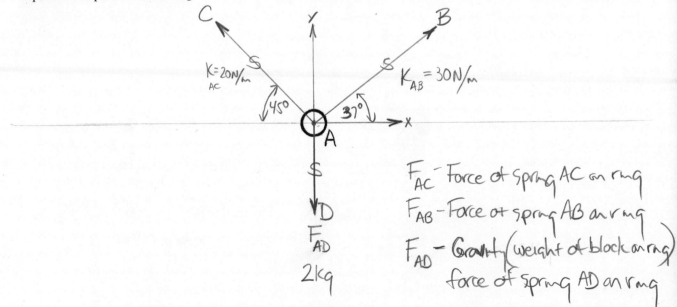

Problem 3.3

The 2-kg block is held in equilibrium by the system of springs. Draw a free-body diagram for the ring at A.

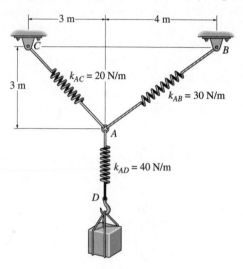

Solution

1. The ring at A has *negligible size* so that it can be modelled as a particle.
2. Imagine the ring at A to be separated or detached from the system.
3. The (detached) ring at A is subjected to three *external* forces. They are caused by:

   i. Spring AD *(weight of block)*   **ii. Spring** AC

   iii. Spring AB

4. Draw the free-body diagram of the (detached) ring showing all these forces labeled with their magnitudes and directions. You should also include any other available information e.g. lengths, angles etc. — which will help when formulating the equilibrium equations for the ring.

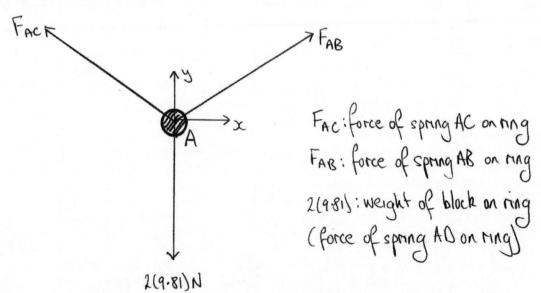

Problem 3.4

The motor at B winds up the cord attached to the 65-lb crate with a constant speed. The force in cord CD supports the pulley C and the angle θ represents the equilibrium state. Draw the free-body diagram of the pulley C. *Neglect the size of the pulley.*

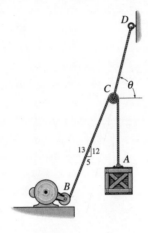

Solution

1. The pulley C has *negligible size* so that it can be modelled as a particle.
2. Imagine the pulley C to be separated or detached from the system.
3. The (detached) pulley C is subjected to three *external* forces. They are caused by:

   i. CD (cord)   **ii.** BC (cord)

   iii. AC (cord) CRATE WEIGHT

4. Draw the free-body diagram of the (detached) pulley showing all these forces labeled with their magnitudes and directions. You should also include any other available information e.g. lengths, angles etc. — which will help when formulating the equilibrium equations for the pulley.

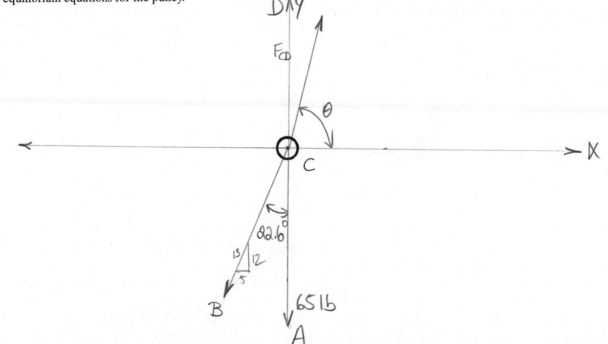

Problem 3.4

The motor at *B* winds up the cord attached to the 65-lb crate with a constant speed. The force in cord *CD* supports the pulley *C* and the angle θ represents the equilibrium state. Draw the free-body diagram of the pulley *C*. *Neglect the size of the pulley*.

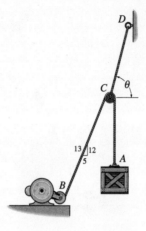

Solution

1. The pulley *C* has *negligible size* so that it can be modelled as a particle.
2. Imagine the pulley *C* to be separated or detached from the system.
3. The (detached) pulley *C* is subjected to three *external* forces. They are caused by:

   i. CORD *CD*   **ii. CORD** *CB*

   iii. CORD *CA (weight of crate)*

4. Draw the free-body diagram of the (detached) pulley showing all these forces labeled with their magnitudes and directions. You should also include any other available information e.g. lengths, angles etc. — which will help when formulating the equilibrium equations for the pulley.

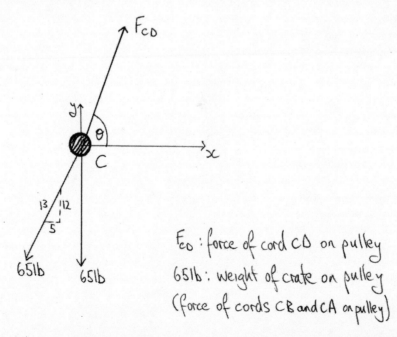

Problem 3.5

The following system is held in equilibrium by the mass supported at A and the angle θ of the connecting cord. Draw the free-body diagram for the connecting knot D.

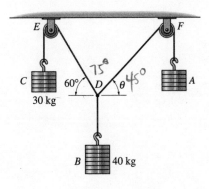

Solution

1. The knot D has *negligible size* so that it can be modelled as a particle.
2. Imagine the knot D to be separated or detached from the system.
3. The (detached) knot D is subjected to three *external* forces. They are caused by:

   i. DE (weight of C)   ii. DF (weight of A)
   iii. DB (weight)

4. Draw the free-body diagram of the (detached) knot showing all these forces labeled with their magnitudes and directions. You should also include any other available information e.g. lengths, angles etc. — which will help when formulating the equilibrium equations for the knot.

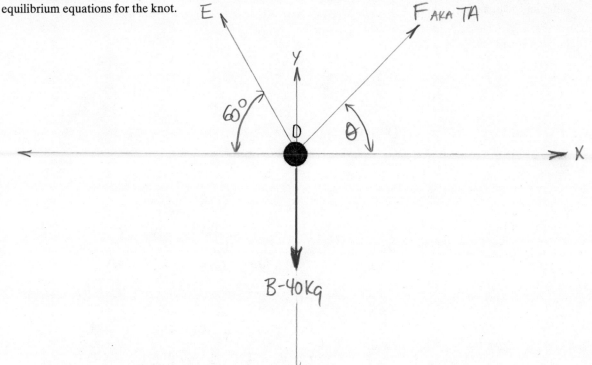

Problem 3.5

The following system is held in equilibrium by the mass supported at A and the angle θ of the connecting cord. Draw the free-body diagram for the connecting knot D.

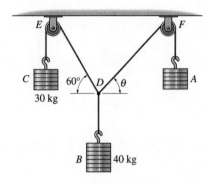

Solution

1. The knot D has *negligible size* so that it can be modelled as a particle.
2. Imagine the knot D to be separated or detached from the system.
3. The (detached) knot D is subjected to three *external* forces. They are caused by:

   i. CORD DE *(weight of C)*   **ii. CORD** DF *(weight of A)*

   iii. CORD DB *(weight of B)*

4. Draw the free-body diagram of the (detached) knot showing all these forces labeled with their magnitudes and directions. You should also include any other available information e.g. lengths, angles etc. — which will help when formulating the equilibrium equations for the knot.

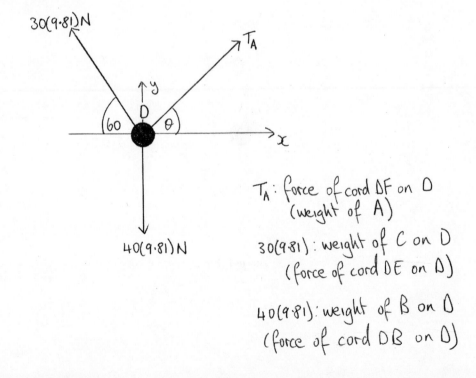

Problem 3.6

The 500 lb crate is hoisted using the ropes AB and AC. Each rope can withstand a maximum tension of 2500 lb before it breaks. Rope AB always remains horizontal. Draw the free-body diagram for the ring at A and determine the smallest angle θ to which the crate can be hoisted.

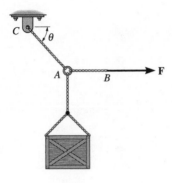

Solution

1. The ring at A has *negligible size* so that it can be modelled as a particle.
2. Imagine the ring at A to be separated or detached from the system.
3. The (detached) ring A is subjected to three *external* forces. They are caused by:

   i. F_{AB} **ii.** F_{AC}

   iii. weight of crate

4. Draw the free-body diagram of the (detached) ring showing all these forces labeled with their magnitudes and directions.

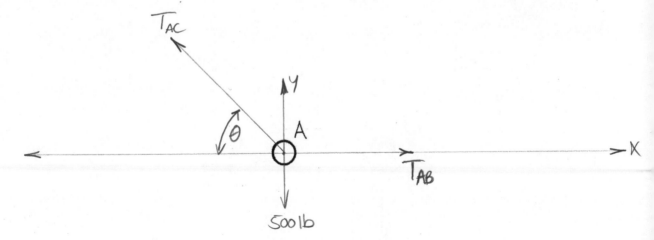

5. Establish an xy-axes system on the free-body diagram and write down the equilibrium equations in each of the x and y-directions

$$+\uparrow \sum F_y = 0: \quad T_{AC} \sin\theta - 500 = 0$$
$$+\underset{\rightarrow}{} \sum F_x = 0: \quad T_{AB} - T_{AC} \cos\theta = 0$$

6. Solve for the angle θ:

Problem 3.6

The 500 lb crate is hoisted using the ropes AB and AC. Each rope can withstand a maximum tension of 2500 lb before it breaks. Rope AB always remains horizontal. Draw the free-body diagram for the ring at A and determine the smallest angle θ to which the crate can be hoisted.

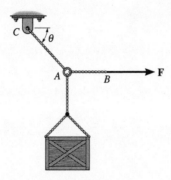

Solution

1. The ring at A has *negligible size* so that it can be modelled as a particle.
2. Imagine the ring at A to be separated or detached from the system.
3. The (detached) ring A is subjected to three *external* forces. They are caused by:

   i. CORD AC **ii. CORD** AB

   iii. CORD AD *(weight of crate)*

4. Draw the free-body diagram of the (detached) ring showing all these forces labeled with their magnitudes and directions.

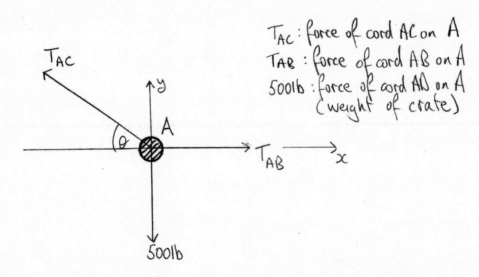

T_{AC}: force of cord AC on A
T_{AB}: force of cord AB on A
500 lb: force of cord AD on A (weight of crate)

5. Establish an xy-axes system on the free-body diagram and write down the equilibrium equations in each of the x and y-directions

$$+\uparrow \sum F_y = 0: \ T_{AC}\sin\theta - 500 = 0$$
$$+_{\rightarrow} \sum F_x = 0: \ T_{AB} - T_{AC}\cos\theta = 0$$

6. Solve for the angle θ:

Assume $T_{AC} = 2500 \text{ lb} \Rightarrow \theta = 11.54°$ and $T_{AB} = 2449.49 \text{ lb} < 2500 \text{ lb (O.K!)}$ **Ans.**

Problem 3.7

The block has a weight of 20 lb and is being hoisted at uniform velocity. The system is held in equilibrium at angle θ by the appropriate force in each cord. Draw the free-body diagram for the *small* pulley.

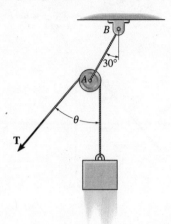

Solution

1. The pulley has *negligible size* so that it can be modelled as a particle.
2. Imagine the pulley to be separated or detached from the system.
3. The (detached) pulley is subjected to three *external* forces. They are caused by:

    i.   **ii.**

    iii.

4. Draw the free-body diagram of the (detached) pulley showing all these forces labeled with their magnitudes and directions. You should also include any other available information e.g. lengths, angles etc. — which will help when formulating the equilibrium equations for the knot.

 A

Problem 3.7

The block has a weight of 20 lb and is being hoisted at uniform velocity. The system is held in equilibrium at angle θ by the appropriate force in each cord. Draw the free-body diagram for the *small* pulley.

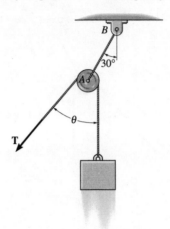

Solution

1. The pulley has *negligible size* so that it can be modelled as a particle.
2. Imagine the pulley to be separated or detached from the system.
3. The (detached) pulley is subjected to three *external* forces. They are caused by:

      i. Cord AB   **ii. Force T**

      iii. Weight of block

4. Draw the free-body diagram of the (detached) pulley showing all these forces labeled with their magnitudes and directions. You should also include any other available information e.g. lengths, angles etc. — which will help when formulating the equilibrium equations for the knot.

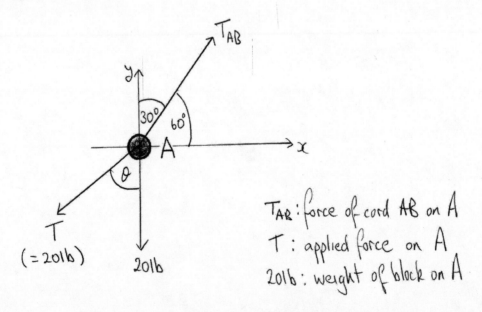

Problem 3.8

Blocks D and F weigh 5 lb each and block E weighs 8 lb. The system is in equilibrium at a given sag s. Draw the free-body diagram for the connecting ring at A and find s. Neglect the size of the pulleys.

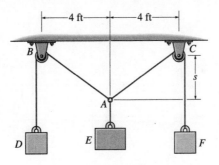

Solution

1. The ring at A has *negligible size* so that it can be modelled as a particle.
2. Imagine the ring to be separated or detached from the system.
3. The (detached) ring is subjected to three *external* forces. They are caused by:

   i.   ii.

   iii.

4. Draw the free-body diagram of the (detached) ring showing all these forces labeled with their magnitudes and directions. Include also any other information which may help when formulating the equilibrium equations for the ring.

5. Establish an xy-axes system on the free-body diagram and write down the equilibrium equations in the y-direction only (this is all that is required to solve this problem):

   $+\uparrow \sum F_y = 0$:

6. Solve for the sag s:

Problem 3.8

Blocks D and F weigh 5 lb each and block E weighs 8 lb. The system is in equilibrium at a given sag s. Draw the free-body diagram for the connecting ring at A and find s. Neglect the size of the pulleys.

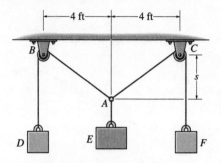

Solution

1. The ring at A has *negligible size* so that it can be modelled as a particle.
2. Imagine the ring to be separated or detached from the system.
3. The (detached) ring is subjected to three *external* forces. They are caused by:

    i. CORD AB *(weight of D)*   **ii. CORD** AC *(weight of F)*

    iii. CORD AE *(weight of E)*

4. Draw the free-body diagram of the (detached) ring showing all these forces labeled with their magnitudes and directions. Include also any other information which may help when formulating the equilibrium equations for the ring.

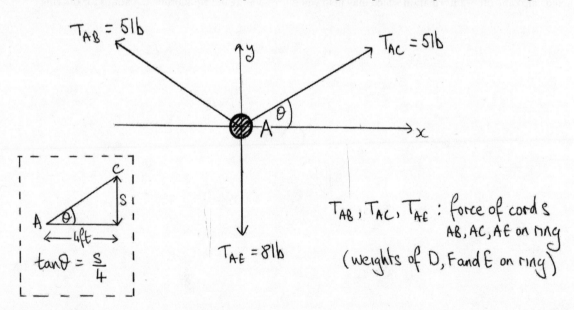

5. Establish an xy-axes system on the free-body diagram and write down the equilibrium equations in the y-direction only (this is all that is required to solve this problem):

$$+\uparrow \sum F_y = 0: \quad 2(5)\sin\theta - 8 = 0 \Rightarrow \theta = 53.13°$$

6. Solve for the sag s:

$$\tan\theta = \frac{s}{4} \Rightarrow s = 4\tan 53.13° = 5.33 \text{ ft} \qquad \textbf{Ans.}$$

Problem 3.9

 A vertical force **P** is applied to the ends of the cord AB and spring AC. The spring has an unstretched length of 2-ft and the system is in equilibrium at angle θ. Draw the free-body diagram of the connecting knot at A and write down the equilibrium equations for the knot at A.

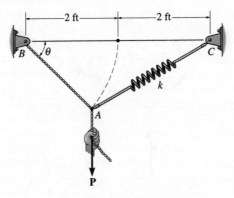

Solution

1. The knot at A has *negligible size* so that it can be modelled as a particle.
2. Imagine the knot at A to be separated or detached from the system.
3. The (detached) knot at A is subjected to three *external* forces. They are caused by:

   i.   **ii.**

   iii.

4. Draw the free-body diagram of the (detached) knot showing all these forces labeled with their magnitudes and directions.

5. Establish an xy-axes system on the free-body diagram and write down the equilibrium equations in each of the x and y-directions

$$+\uparrow \sum F_y = 0:$$
$$\underset{\rightarrow}{+} \sum F_x = 0:$$

Problem 3.9

A vertical force **P** is applied to the ends of the cord AB and spring AC. The spring has an unstretched length of 2-ft and the system is in equilibrium at angle θ. Draw the free-body diagram of the connecting knot at A and write down the equilibrium equations for the knot at A.

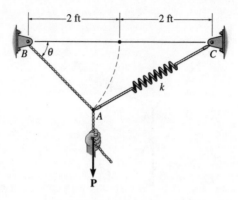

Solution

1. The knot at A has *negligible size* so that it can be modelled as a particle.
2. Imagine the knot at A to be separated or detached from the system.
3. The (detached) knot at A is subjected to three *external* forces. They are caused by:

   i. CORD AB 　　　　　　　　　　　　　　**ii. SPRING** AC

   iii. Force P

4. Draw the free-body diagram of the (detached) knot showing all these forces labeled with their magnitudes and directions.

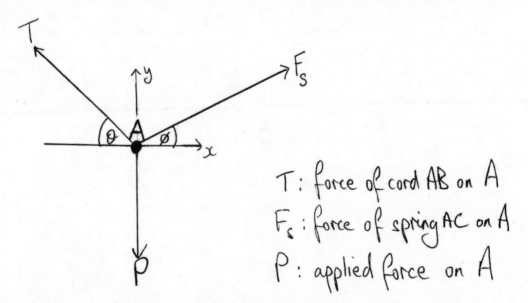

5. Establish an xy-axes system on the free-body diagram and write down the equilibrium equations in each of the x and y-directions

$$\underset{\rightarrow}{+} \sum F_x = 0: \quad F_s \cos \phi - T \cos \theta = 0$$

$$+ \uparrow \sum F_y = 0: \quad T \sin \theta + F_s \sin \phi - P = 0$$

Ans.

Problem 3.10

The sling BAC is used to lift the 100-lb load with constant velocity. By drawing the free-body diagram for the ring at A, determine the magnitude of the force in the sling as a function of the angle θ.

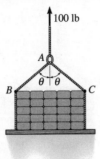

100 lb

Solution

1. The ring at A has *negligible size* so that it can be modelled as a particle.
2. Imagine the ring at A to be separated or detached from the system.
3. The (detached) ring at A is subjected to three *external* forces. They are caused by:

   i.   **ii.**

   iii.

4. Draw the free-body diagram of the (detached) ring showing all these forces labeled with their magnitudes and directions. Include also any other information which may help when formulating the equilibrium equations for the ring.

A

5. Establish an xy-axes system on the free-body diagram and write down the equilibrium equations in the y-direction only (this is all that is required to solve this problem):

   $+\uparrow \sum F_y = 0:$

6. Solve for the magnitude of the force in the sling:

Problem 3.10

The sling BAC is used to lift the 100-lb load with constant velocity. By drawing the free-body diagram for the ring at A, determine the magnitude of the force in the sling as a function of the angle θ.

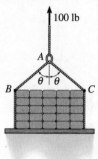

Solution

1. The ring at A has *negligible size* so that it can be modelled as a particle.
2. Imagine the ring at A to be separated or detached from the system.
3. The (detached) ring at A is subjected to three *external* forces. They are caused by:
   - **i. CORD** AB **ii. CORD** AC
   - **iii. CORD** AD *(weight of load)*
4. Draw the free-body diagram of the (detached) ring showing all these forces labeled with their magnitudes and directions. Include also any other information which may help when formulating the equilibrium equations for the ring.

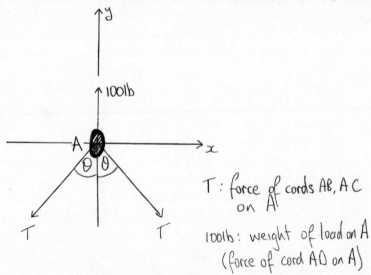

5. Establish an xy-axes system on the free-body diagram and write down the equilibrium equations in the y-direction only (this is all that is required to solve this problem):

$$+\uparrow \sum F_y = 0: \quad 100 - 2T\cos\theta = 0$$

6. Solve for the magnitude of the force in the sling:

$$T = \frac{50}{\cos\theta}$$

Ans.

Problem 3.11

When y is zero, the springs sustain a force of 60 lb. The applied vertical forces **F** and **−F** pull the point A away from B a distance of $y = 2$ ft. The cords CAD and CBD are attached to the rings at C and D. Draw the free-body diagrams for point A and ring C.

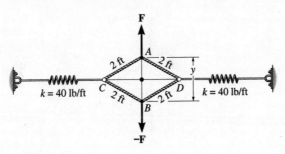

Solution

1. Imagine A and C to be separated or detached from the system.
2. Each of A and C is subjected to three *external* forces. For A, they are caused by:

   i.   **ii.**

   iii.

   For C, they are caused by:

   i.   **ii.**

   iii.

3. Draw the free-body diagrams of A and C showing all these forces labeled with their magnitudes and directions. You should also include any other available information e.g. lengths, angles etc. — which will help when formulating the equilibrium equations.

• A

o
C

Problem 3.11

When y is zero, the springs sustain a force of 60 lb. The applied vertical forces **F** and −**F** pull the point A away from B a distance of $y = 2$ ft. The cords CAD and CBD are attached to the rings at C and D. Draw the free-body diagrams for point A and ring C.

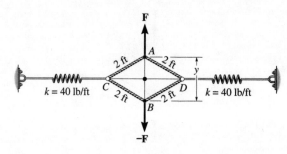

Solution

1. Imagine A and C to be separated or detached from the system.
2. Each of A and C is subjected to three *external* forces. For A, they are caused by:

   i. CORD AC **ii. CORD** AD

   iii. Force F

   For C, they are caused by:

   i. CORD AC **ii. CORD** CB

   iii. Spring attached at C

3. Draw the free-body diagrams of A and C showing all these forces labeled with their magnitudes and directions. You should also include any other available information e.g. lengths, angles etc. — which will help when formulating the equilibrium equations.

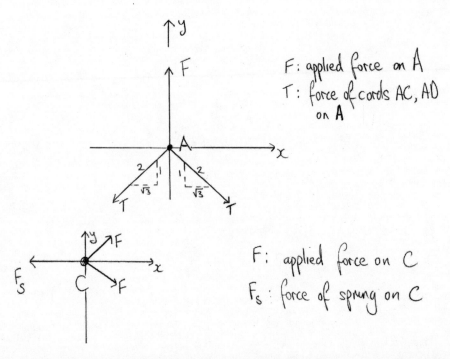

Problem 3.12

By drawing a free-body diagram for the ring at A, determine the maximum weight W that can be supported in the position shown if each cable AC and AB can support a maximum tension of 600 lb before it fails.

Solution

1. The ring at A has *negligible size* so that it can be modelled as a particle.
2. Imagine the ring at A to be separated or detached from the system.
3. The (detached) ring at A is subjected to three *external* forces. They are caused by:

   i.   ii.

   iii.

4. Draw the free-body diagram of the (detached) ring showing all these forces labeled with their magnitudes and directions. Include any other relevant information e.g. lengths, angles etc.

$$A\bigcirc$$

5. Establish an xy-axes system on the free-body diagram and write down the equilibrium equations in each of the x and y-directions

$$+\uparrow \sum F_y = 0:$$

$$+\rightarrow \sum F_x = 0:$$

6. Set the tension in AB to the maximum of 600 lb and solve for the maximum weight W:

Problem 3.12

By drawing a free-body diagram for the ring at A, determine the maximum weight $\mathbf{W}$ that can be supported in the position shown if each cable AC and AB can support a maximum tension of 600 lb before it fails.

Solution

1. The ring at A has *negligible size* so that it can be modelled as a particle.
2. Imagine the ring at A to be separated or detached from the system.
3. The (detached) ring at A is subjected to three *external* forces. They are caused by:

    i. CABLE AB   **ii. CABLE AB**

    iii. Weight of ball

4. Draw the free-body diagram of the (detached) ring showing all these forces labeled with their magnitudes and directions. Include any other relevant information e.g. lengths, angles etc.

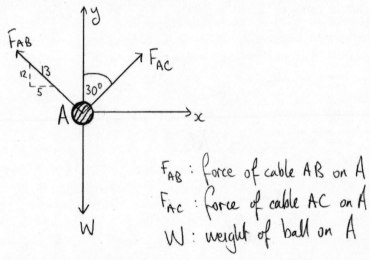

5. Establish an xy-axes system on the free-body diagram and write down the equilibrium equations in each of the x and y-directions

$$\underset{\rightarrow}{+}\sum F_x = 0: \quad -F_{AB}\left(\frac{5}{13}\right) + F_{AC}\sin 30° = 0$$

$$+\uparrow \sum F_y = 0: \quad F_{AB}\left(\frac{12}{13}\right) + F_{AC}\cos 30° - W = 0$$

6. Set F_{AB}, the tension in AB, to the maximum of 600 lb and solve for the maximum weight $\mathbf{W}$:

$$F_{AC} = 461.54 \text{ lb}(< 600 \text{ lb!!}), \quad \mathbf{W} = 953.55 \text{ lb} \downarrow \qquad\qquad \textbf{Ans.}$$

Problem 3.13

The cords suspend the two *small* buckets in the equilibrium position shown. Draw the free-body diagrams for each of the points F and C.

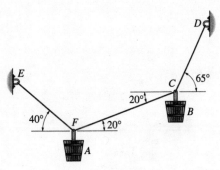

Solution

1. Imagine the points F and C to be separated or detached from the system.

2. Each of F and C is subjected to three *external* forces. For F, they are caused by:

   i.   **ii.**

   iii.

   For C, they are caused by:

   i.   **ii.**

   iii.

3. Draw the free-body diagrams of F and C showing all these forces labeled with their magnitudes and directions. You should also include any other available information e.g. lengths, angles etc. — which will help when formulating the equilibrium equations at these points.

$_\bullet F$

$\bullet$

C

Problem 3.13

The cords suspend the two *small* buckets in the equilibrium position shown. Draw the free-body diagrams for each of the points F and C.

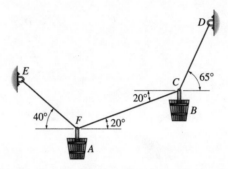

Solution

1. Imagine the points F and C to be separated or detached from the system.
2. Each of F and C is subjected to three *external* forces. For F, they are caused by:

   i. CABLE FE **ii. CABLE** FC

   iii. Weight of A

   For C, they are caused by:

   i. CABLE CF **ii. CABLE** CD

   iii. Weight of B

3. Draw the free-body diagrams of F and C showing all these forces labeled with their magnitudes and directions. You should also include any other available information e.g. lengths, angles etc. — which will help when formulating the equilibrium equations at these points.

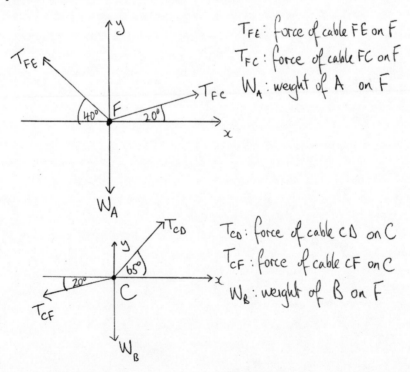

Problem 3.14

The 30-kg pipe is supported at A by a system of five cords. Draw the free-body diagrams for the rings at A and B when the system is in equilibrium.

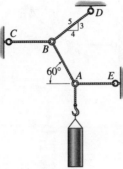

Solution

1. Imagine A and B to be separated or detached from the system.
2. Each of A and B is subjected to three *external* forces. For A, they are caused by:

   i.   **ii.**

   iii.

   For B, they are caused by:

   i.   **ii.**

   iii.

3. Draw the free-body diagrams of A and B showing all these forces labeled with their magnitudes and directions. You should also include any other available information e.g. lengths, angles etc. — which will help when formulating the equilibrium equations.

Problem 3.14

The 30-kg pipe is supported at A by a system of five cords. Draw the free-body diagrams for the rings at A and B when the system is in equilibrium.

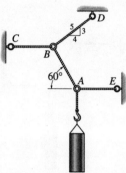

Solution

1. Imagine A and B to be separated or detached from the system.
2. Each of A and B is subjected to three *external* forces. For A, they are caused by:

   i. CABLE AB **ii. CABLE** AE

   iii. Weight of Pipe

For B, they are caused by:

   i. CABLE BC **ii. CABLE** BD

   iii. CABLE BA

3. Draw the free-body diagrams of A and B showing all these forces labeled with their magnitudes and directions. You should also include any other available information e.g. lengths, angles etc. — which will help when formulating the equilibrium equations.

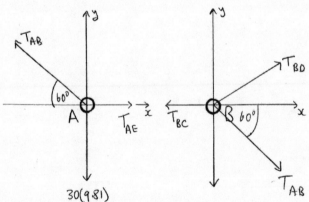

Problem 3.15

The cord AB has a length of 5 ft and is attached to the end B of the spring having a stiffness $k = 10$ lb/ft. The other end of the spring is attached to a roller C so that the spring remains horizontal as it stretches. If a 10-lb weight is suspended from B, use the free-body diagram for the ring at B to determine the necessary unstretched length of the spring, so that $\theta = 40°$ for equilibrium.

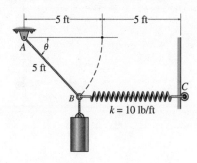

Solution

1. Imagine the ring at B to be separated or detached from the system.
2. The (detached) ring at B is subjected to three *external* forces caused by:

   i.   **ii.**

   iii.

3. Draw the free-body diagram of the (detached) ring showing all these forces labeled with their magnitudes and directions. Include any other relevant information e.g. lengths, angles etc.

4. Establish an xy-axes system on the free-body diagram and write down the equilibrium equations in each of the x and y-directions

$$+\uparrow \sum F_y = 0:$$

$$\underset{\rightarrow}{+} \sum F_x = 0:$$

5. Determine the stretch in the spring BC and solve for the necessary unstretched length:

Problem 3.15

The cord AB has a length of 5 ft and is attached to the end B of the spring having a stiffness $k = 10$ lb/ft. The other end of the spring is attached to a roller C so that the spring remains horizontal as it stretches. If a 10-lb weight is suspended from B, use the free-body diagram for the ring at B to determine the necessary unstretched length of the spring, so that $\theta = 40°$ for equilibrium.

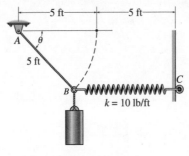

Solution

1. Imagine the ring at B to be separated or detached from the system.

2. The (detached) ring at B is subjected to three *external* forces caused by:

   i. **CABLE** AB ii. **SPRING** BC

   iii. **10 lb Weight**

3. Draw the free-body diagram of the (detached) ring showing all these forces labeled with their magnitudes and directions. Include any other relevant information e.g. lengths, angles etc.

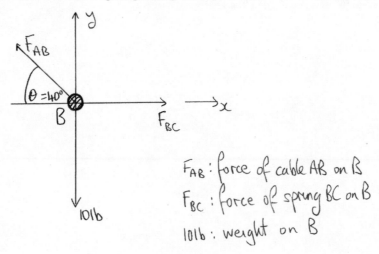

F_{AB} : force of cable AB on B

F_{BC} : force of spring BC on B

10 lb : weight on B

4. Establish an xy-axes system on the free-body diagram and write down the equilibrium equations in each of the x and y-directions

$$+\uparrow \sum F_y = 0: \; F_{AB} \sin 40° - 10 = 0 \Rightarrow F_{AB} = 15.557 \text{ lb}$$

$$\underset{\rightarrow}{+} \sum F_x = 0: \; F_{BC} - F_{AB} \cos 40° = 0 \Rightarrow F_{BC} = 11.918 \text{ lb}$$

5. Determine the stretch in the spring BC and solve for the necessary unstretched length l:

$$F_{BC} = kx \Rightarrow x = \frac{11.918}{10} = 1.1918 \text{ ft (stretch in } BC)$$

$$BC = 5 + (5 - 5 \cos 40°) = 6.17 \text{ ft}$$

$$l = 6.17 - 1.1918 = 4.98 \text{ ft}$$ **Ans.**

3.2 Free-Body Diagrams in the Equilibrium of a Rigid Body

Problem 3.16

Draw the free-body diagram of the 50-kg uniform pipe, which is supported by the smooth contacts at A and B.

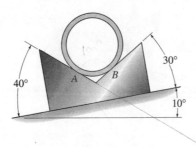

Solution

1. Imagine the pipe to be separated or detached from the system.
2. The supports at A and B are smooth contacts. Use Table 2.1 (6) to determine the number and types of reactions *acting on the pipe* at A and B.
3. The pipe is subjected to three *external* forces (don't forget the weight!). They are caused by:

   i.   **ii.**

   iii.

4. Draw the free-body diagram of the (detached) pipe showing all these forces labeled with their magnitudes and directions. *Assume* the sense of the vectors representing the *reactions acting on the pipe* (the correct sense will always emerge from the equilibrium equations for the pipe). Include any other relevant information e.g. lengths, angles etc. which may help when formulating the equilibrium equations (including the moment equation) for the pipe.

Problem 3.16

Draw the free-body diagram of the 50-kg uniform pipe, which is supported by the smooth contacts at A and B.

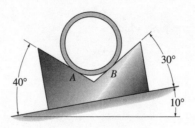

Solution

1. Imagine the pipe to be separated or detached from the system.
2. The supports at A and B are smooth contacts. Use Table 2.1 (6) to determine the number and types of reactions *acting on the pipe* at A and B.
3. The pipe is subjected to three *external* forces (don't forget the weight!). They are caused by:

   i. **The reaction at** A ii. **The reaction at** B

   iii. **The weight of the pipe**

4. Draw the free-body diagram of the (detached) pipe showing all these forces labeled with their magnitudes and directions. *Assume* the sense of the vectors representing the *reactions acting on the pipe* (the correct sense will always emerge from the equilibrium equations for the pipe). Include any other relevant information e.g. lengths, angles etc. which may help when formulating the equilibrium equations (including the moment equation) for the pipe.

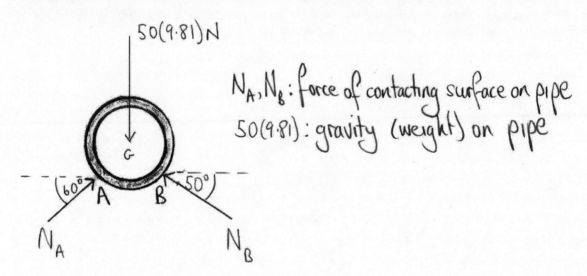

Problem 3.17

Draw the free-body diagram of the hand punch, which is pinned at A and bears down on the smooth surface at B. Neglect the weight of the punch.

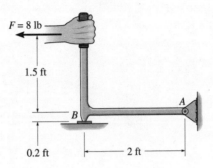

Solution

1. Imagine the hand punch to be separated or detached from the system.
2. The support at B is a smooth contact. The punch is (smoothly) pin-connected at A. Use Table 2.1 (6) and (8) to determine the number and types of reactions *acting on the pipe* at A and B.
3. The punch is subjected to four *external* forces. They are caused by:

   i.   **ii.**

   iii.   **iv.**

4. Draw the free-body diagram of the (detached) punch showing all these forces labeled with their magnitudes and directions. *Assume* the sense of the vectors representing the *reactions acting on the punch* (the correct sense will always emerge from the equilibrium equations for the punch). Include any other relevant information e.g. lengths, angles etc. which may help when formulating the equilibrium equations (including the moment equation) for the punch.

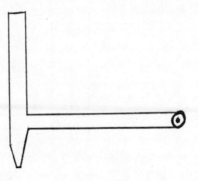

Problem 3.17

Draw the free-body diagram of the hand punch, which is pinned at A and bears down on the smooth surface at B. Neglect the weight of the punch.

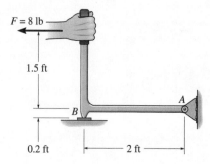

Solution

1. Imagine the hand punch to be separated or detached from the system.
2. The support at B is a smooth contact. The punch is (smoothly) pin-connected at A. Use Table 2.1 (6) and (8) to determine the number and types of reactions *acting on the pipe* at A and B.
3. The punch is subjected to four *external* forces. They are caused by:

   i. The force F   **ii. The reaction at B**

   iii. & iv. The two reactions at A

4. Draw the free-body diagram of the (detached) punch showing all these forces labeled with their magnitudes and directions. *Assume* the sense of the vectors representing the *reactions acting on the punch* (the correct sense will always emerge from the equilibrium equations for the punch). Include any other relevant information e.g. lengths, angles etc. which may help when formulating the equilibrium equations (including the moment equation) for the punch.

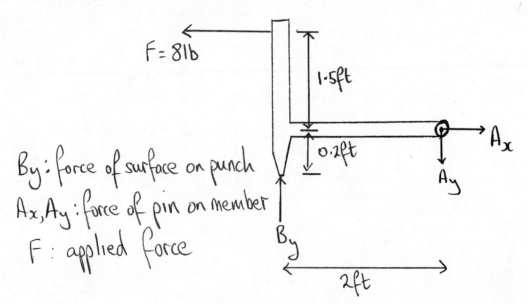

Problem 3.18

Draw the free-body diagram of the jib crane AB, which is pin-connected at A and supported by member (link) BC. Neglect the weight of the crane.

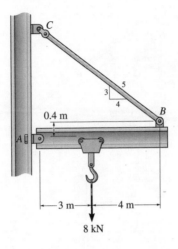

Solution

1. Imagine the jib crane AB to be separated or detached from the system.
2. There is a link support at B and the jib crane is (smoothly) pinned at A. Use Table 2.1 (2) and (8) to determine the number and types of reactions *acting on the jib crane* at A and B.
3. The jib crane is subjected to four *external* forces. They are caused by:

   i.   ii.

   iii.   iv.

4. Draw the free-body diagram of the (detached) crane showing all these forces labeled with their magnitudes and directions. *Assume* the sense of the vectors representing the *reactions acting on the crane* (the correct sense will always emerge from the equilibrium equations for the crane). Include any other relevant information e.g. lengths, angles etc. which may help when formulating the equilibrium equations (including the moment equation) for the jib crane.

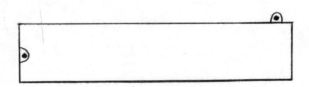

Problem 3.18

Draw the free-body diagram of the jib crane AB, which is pin-connected at A and supported by member (link) BC. Neglect the weight of the crane.

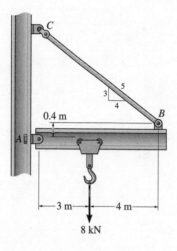

Solution

1. Imagine the jib crane AB to be separated or detached from the system.
2. There is a link support at B and the jib crane is (smoothly) pinned at A. Use Table 2.1 (2) and (8) to determine the number and types of reactions *acting on the jib crane* at A and B.
3. The jib crane is subjected to four *external* forces. They are caused by:

   i. & ii. The reactions at A   **iii. The reaction at B**

   iv. The 8 kN load

4. Draw the free-body diagram of the (detached) crane showing all these forces labeled with their magnitudes and directions. *Assume* the sense of the vectors representing the *reactions acting on the crane* (the correct sense will always emerge from the equilibrium equations for the crane). Include any other relevant information e.g. lengths, angles etc. which may help when formulating the equilibrium equations (including the moment equation) for the jib crane.

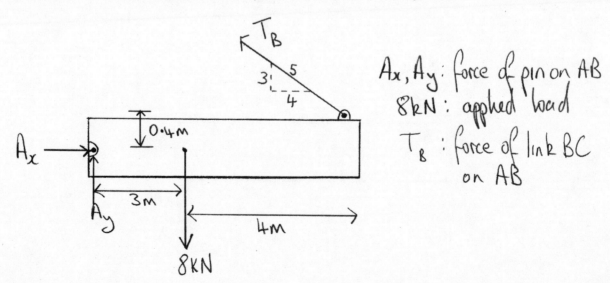

Problem 3.19

Draw the free-body diagram of the dumpster D of the truck, which has a weight of 5000 lb and a center of gravity at G. It is supported by a pin at A and a pin-connected hydraulic cylinder BC (short link).

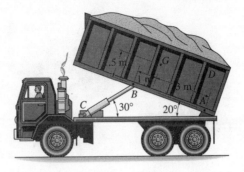

Solution

1. Imagine the dumpster D to be separated or detached from the truck.
2. There is a pin support at A and the dumpster is supported by a short link support at B. Use Table 2.1 (2) and (8) to determine the number and types of reactions *acting on the dumpster* at A and B.
3. The dumpster is subjected to four *external* forces. They are caused by:

   i.   ii.

   iii.   iv.

4. Draw the free-body diagram of the (detached) dumpster showing all these forces labeled with their magnitudes and directions. *Assume* the sense of the vectors representing the *reactions acting on the dumpster* (the correct sense will always emerge from the equilibrium equations for the dumpster). Include any other relevant information e.g. lengths, angles etc. which may help when formulating the equilibrium equations (including the moment equation) for the dumpster.

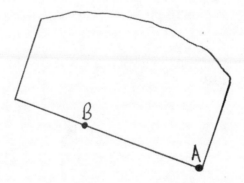

Problem 3.19

Draw the free-body diagram of the dumpster D of the truck, which has a weight of 5000 lb and a center of gravity at G. It is supported by a pin at A and a pin-connected hydraulic cylinder BC (short link).

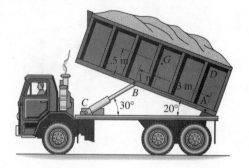

Solution

1. Imagine the dumpster D to be separated or detached from the truck.

2. There is a pin support at A and the dumpster is supported by a short link support at B. Use Table 2.1 (2) and (8) to determine the number and types of reactions *acting on the dumpster* at A and B.

3. The dumpster is subjected to four *external* forces. They are caused by:

    i. & ii. The reactions at A   **iii. The reaction at B**

    iv. The weight of the dumpster

4. Draw the free-body diagram of the (detached) dumpster showing all these forces labeled with their magnitudes and directions. *Assume* the sense of the vectors representing the *reactions acting on the dumpster* (the correct sense will always emerge from the equilibrium equations for the dumpster). Include any other relevant information e.g. lengths, angles etc. which may help when formulating the equilibrium equations (including the moment equation) for the dumpster.

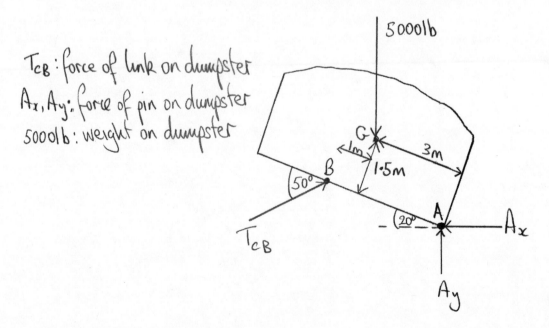

T_{CB}: force of link on dumpster

A_x, A_y: force of pin on dumpster

5000 lb: weight on dumpster

Problem 3.20

Draw the free-body diagram of the link CAB, which is pin-connected at A and rests on the smooth cam at B. Neglect the weight of the link.

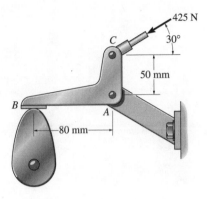

Solution

1. Imagine the link CAB to be separated or detached from the mechanism.
2. There is a pin connection at A and the link rests on the smooth surface at B. Use Table 2.1 (6) and (8) to determine the number and types of reactions *acting on the link* at A and B.
3. The link is subjected to four *external* forces. They are caused by:

    i.   ii.

    iii.   iv.

4. Draw the free-body diagram of the (detached) link showing all these forces labeled with their magnitudes and directions. *Assume* the sense of the vectors representing the *reactions acting on the link* (the correct sense will always emerge from the equilibrium equations for the link). Include any other relevant information e.g. lengths, angles etc. which may help when formulating the equilibrium equations (including the moment equation) for the link.

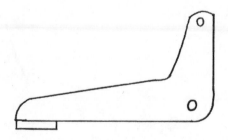

Problem 3.20

Draw the free-body diagram of the link CAB, which is pin-connected at A and rests on the smooth cam at B. Neglect the weight of the link.

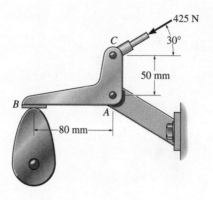

Solution

1. Imagine the link CAB to be separated or detached from the mechanism.
2. There is a pin connection at A and the link rests on the smooth surface at B. Use Table 2.1 (6) and (8) to determine the number and types of reactions *acting on the link* at A and B.
3. The link is subjected to four *external* forces. They are caused by:

   i. & ii. The reactions at A   **iii. The reaction at B**

   iv. The 425 N load at C

4. Draw the free-body diagram of the (detached) link showing all these forces labeled with their magnitudes and directions. *Assume* the sense of the vectors representing the *reactions acting on the link* (the correct sense will always emerge from the equilibrium equations for the link). Include any other relevant information e.g. lengths, angles etc. which may help when formulating the equilibrium equations (including the moment equation) for the link.

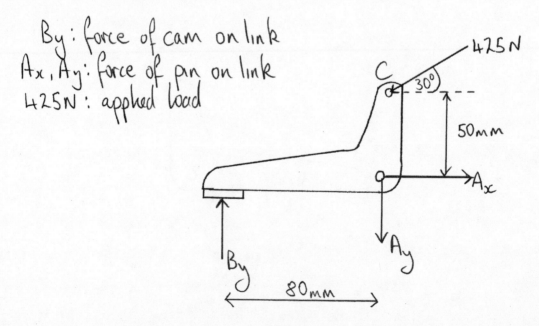

Problem 3.21

Draw the free-body diagram of the uniform pipe which has a mass of 100 kg and a center of mass at G. The supports A, B and C are smooth.

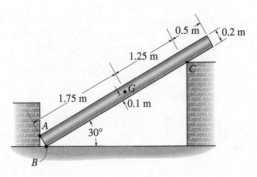

Solution

1. Imagine the pipe to be separated or detached from the system.
2. The pipe rests on smooth surfaces at A, B and C. Use Table 2.1 (6) to determine the number and types of reactions *acting on the pipe* at A, B and C.
3. The pipe is subjected to four *external* forces. They are caused by:

   i.   ii.

   iii.   iv.

4. Draw the free-body diagram of the (detached) pipe showing all these forces labeled with their magnitudes and directions. *Assume* the sense of the vectors representing the *reactions acting on the pipe* (the correct sense will always emerge from the equilibrium equations for the pipe). Include any other relevant information e.g. lengths, angles etc. which may help when formulating the equilibrium equations for the pipe.

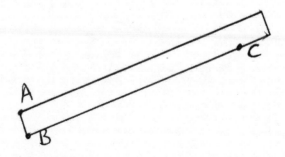

Problem 3.21.

Draw the free-body diagram of the uniform pipe which has a mass of 100 kg and a center of mass at G. The supports A, B and C are smooth.

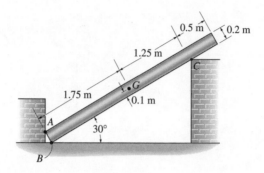

Solution

1. Imagine the pipe to be separated or detached from the system.
2. The pipe rests on smooth surfaces at A, B and C. Use Table 2.1 (6) to determine the number and types of reactions *acting on the pipe* at A, B and C.
3. The pipe is subjected to four *external* forces. They are caused by:

   i. The reaction at A   **ii. The reaction at B**

   iii. The reaction at C   **iv. Pipe's weight**

4. Draw the free-body diagram of the (detached) pipe showing all these forces labeled with their magnitudes and directions. *Assume* the sense of the vectors representing the *reactions acting on the pipe* (the correct sense will always emerge from the equilibrium equations for the pipe). Include any other relevant information e.g. lengths, angles etc. which may help when formulating the equilibrium equations for the pipe.

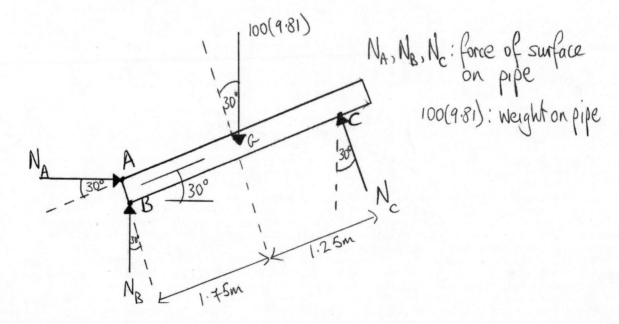

Problem 3.22

Draw the free-body diagram of the beam, which is pin-supported at A and rests on the smooth incline at B. Neglect the weight of the beam.

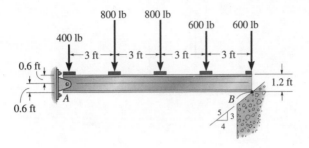

Solution

1. Imagine the beam to be separated or detached from the system.
2. There is a pin connection at A and the beam rests on the smooth (inclined) surface at B. Use Table 2.1 (6) and (8) to determine the number and types of reactions *acting on the beam* at A and B.
3. In addition to the forces shown in the figure, the beam is subjected to three *external* forces. They are caused by:

   i.   **ii.**

   iii.

4. Draw the free-body diagram of the (detached) beam showing all these forces labeled with their magnitudes and directions. *Assume* the sense of the vectors representing the *reactions acting on the beam* (the correct sense will always emerge from the equilibrium equations for the beam). Include any other relevant information e.g. lengths, angles etc. which may help when formulating the equilibrium equations (including the moment equation) for the beam.

Problem 3.22

Draw the free-body diagram of the beam, which is pin-supported at A and rests on the smooth incline at B. Neglect the weight of the beam.

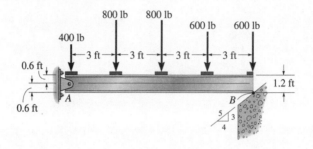

Solution

1. Imagine the beam to be separated or detached from the system.
2. There is a pin connection at A and the beam rests on the smooth (inclined) surface at B. Use Table 2.1 (6) and (8) to determine the number and types of reactions *acting on the beam* at A and B.
3. In addition to the forces shown in the figure, the beam is subjected to three *external* forces. They are caused by:

    i. & ii. The reactions at A   **iii. The reaction at B**

4. Draw the free-body diagram of the (detached) beam showing all these forces labeled with their magnitudes and directions. *Assume* the sense of the vectors representing the *reactions acting on the beam* (the correct sense will always emerge from the equilibrium equations for the beam). Include any other relevant information e.g. lengths, angles etc. which may help when formulating the equilibrium equations (including the moment equation) for the beam.

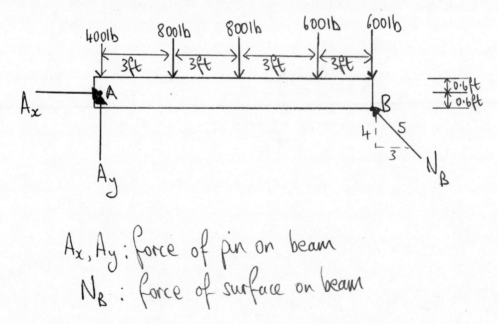

Problem 3.23

Draw the free-body diagram of the member ABC, which is supported by a pin at A and a horizontal short link BD. Neglect the weight of ABC.

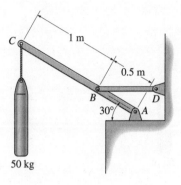

Solution

1. Imagine the member ABC to be separated or detached from the system.
2. There is a pin support at A and the member is supported by a horizontal short link at B. Use Table 2.1 (2) and (8) to determine the number and types of reactions *acting on the member* at A and B.
3. The member is subjected to four *external* forces. They are caused by:

   i.   ii.

   iii.   iv.

4. Draw the free-body diagram of the (detached) member showing all these forces labeled with their magnitudes and directions. *Assume* the sense of the vectors representing the *reactions acting on the member* (the correct sense will always emerge from the equilibrium equations for the member). Include any other relevant information e.g. lengths, angles etc. which may help when formulating the equilibrium equations (including the moment equation) for the member.

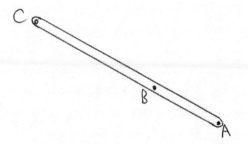

Problem 3.23

Draw the free-body diagram of the member ABC, which is supported by a pin at A and a horizontal short link BD. Neglect the weight of ABC.

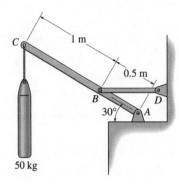

Solution

1. Imagine the member ABC to be separated or detached from the system.
2. There is a pin support at A and the member is supported by a horizontal short link at B. Use Table 2.1 (2) and (8) to determine the number and types of reactions *acting on the member* at A and B.
3. The member is subjected to four *external* forces. They are caused by:

   i. & ii. The reactions at A   **iii. The reaction at B**

   iv. The weight at C

4. Draw the free-body diagram of the (detached) member showing all these forces labeled with their magnitudes and directions. *Assume* the sense of the vectors representing the *reactions acting on the member* (the correct sense will always emerge from the equilibrium equations for the member). Include any other relevant information e.g. lengths, angles etc. which may help when formulating the equilibrium equations (including the moment equation) for the member.

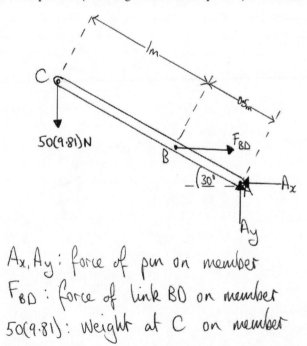

A_x, A_y : force of pin on member

F_{BD} : force of link BD on member

$50(9.81)$: weight at C on member

Problem 3.24

Draw the free-body diagram of the beam. The support at *B* is smooth. Neglect the weight of the beam.

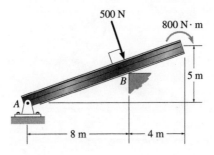

Solution

1. Imagine the beam to be separated or detached from the system.
2. There is a pin support at *A* and a smooth contact support at *B*. Use Table 2.1 (6) and (8) to determine the number and types of reactions *acting on the member* at *A* and *B*.
3. In addition to those shown in the figure, the member is subjected to three *external* forces. They are caused by:

   i.   **ii.**

   iii.

4. Draw the free-body diagram of the (detached) member showing all these forces and any external applied couple moments labeled with their magnitudes and directions. *Assume* the sense of the vectors representing the *reactions acting on the member* (the correct sense will always emerge from the equilibrium equations for the member). Include any other relevant information e.g. lengths, angles etc. which may help when formulating the equilibrium equations (including the moment equation) for the member.

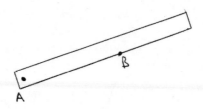

Problem 3.24

Draw the free-body diagram of the beam. The support at B is smooth. Neglect the weight of the beam.

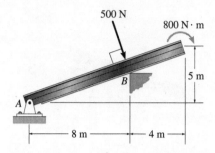

Solution

1. Imagine the beam to be separated or detached from the system.

2. There is a pin support at A and a smooth contact support at B. Use Table 2.1 (6) and (8) to determine the number and types of reactions *acting on the member* at A and B.

3. In addition to those shown in the figure, the member is subjected to three *external* forces. They are caused by:

   i. & ii. The reactions at A **iii. The reaction at** B

4. Draw the free-body diagram of the (detached) member showing all these forces and any external applied couple moments labeled with their magnitudes and directions. *Assume* the sense of the vectors representing the *reactions acting on the member* (the correct sense will always emerge from the equilibrium equations for the member). Include any other relevant information e.g. lengths, angles etc. which may help when formulating the equilibrium equations (including the moment equation) for the member.

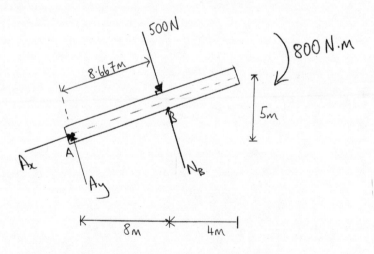

Problem 3.25

Draw the free-body diagram of the vehicle, which has a mass of 5 Mg and center of mass at G. The tires are free to roll, so rolling resistance can be neglected.

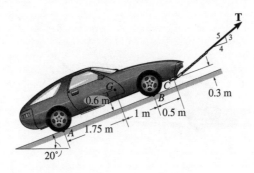

Solution

1. Imagine the vehicle to be separated or detached from the system.
2. There are smooth contacts at A and B. Use Table 2.1 (6) to determine the number and types of reactions *acting on the vehicle* at A and B.
3. The vehicle is subjected to four *external* forces. They are caused by:

   i.   **ii.**

   iii.   **iv.**

4. Draw the free-body diagram of the (detached) vehicle showing all these forces labeled with their magnitudes and directions. *Assume* the sense of the vectors representing the *reactions acting on the vehicle* (the correct sense will always emerge from the equilibrium equations for the vehicle). Include any other relevant information e.g. lengths, angles etc. which may help when formulating the equilibrium equations (including the moment equation) for the vehicle.

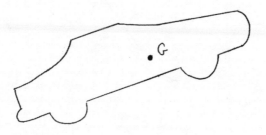

Problem 3.25

Draw the free-body diagram of the vehicle, which has a mass of 5 Mg and center of mass at G. The tires are free to roll, so rolling resistance can be neglected.

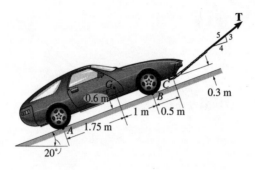

Solution

1. Imagine the vehicle to be separated or detached from the system.
2. There are smooth contacts at A and B. Use Table 2.1 (6) to determine the number and types of reactions *acting on the vehicle* at A and B.
3. The vehicle is subjected to four *external* forces. They are caused by:

       i. The reaction at A   **ii. The reaction at B**

      iii. Car's weight   **iv. Force T**

4. Draw the free-body diagram of the (detached) vehicle showing all these forces labeled with their magnitudes and directions. *Assume* the sense of the vectors representing the *reactions acting on the vehicle* (the correct sense will always emerge from the equilibrium equations for the vehicle). Include any other relevant information e.g. lengths, angles etc. which may help when formulating the equilibrium equations (including the moment equation) for the vehicle.

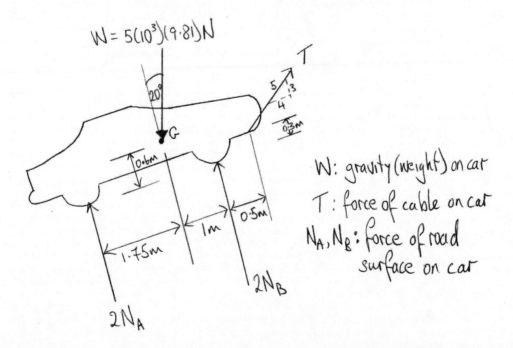

Problem 3.26

Draw a free-body diagram of the crane boom ABC, which has a mass of 45 kg, center of gravity at G, and supports a load of 30 Kg. The boom is pin-connected to the frame at B and connected to a vertical chain CD. The chain supporting the load is attached to the boom at A.

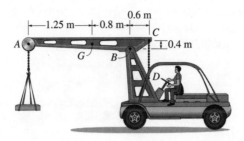

Solution

1. Imagine the boom to be separated or detached from the system.
2. There is a pin connection at B and a vertical chain (cable) support at C. Use Table 2.1 (1) and (8) to determine the number and types of reactions *acting on the boom* at B and C.
3. The boom is subjected to five *external* forces. They are caused by:

   i.   **ii.**

   iii.   **iv.**

   v.

4. Draw the free-body diagram of the (detached) boom showing all these forces labeled with their magnitudes and directions. *Assume* the sense of the vectors representing the *reactions acting on the boom*. Include any other relevant information e.g. lengths, angles etc. which may help when formulating the equilibrium equations (including the moment equation) for the boom.

Problem 3.26

Draw a free-body diagram of the crane boom ABC, which has a mass of 45 kg, center of gravity at G, and supports a load of 30 Kg. The boom is pin-connected to the frame at B and connected to a vertical chain CD. The chain supporting the load is attached to the boom at A.

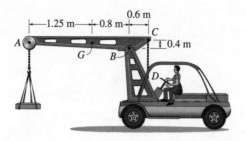

Solution

1. Imagine the boom to be separated or detached from the system.
2. There is a pin connection at B and a vertical chain (cable) support at C. Use Table 2.1 (1) and (8) to determine the number and types of reactions *acting on the boom* at B and C.
3. The boom is subjected to five *external* forces. They are caused by:

   i. & ii. The reactions at B   **iii. The reaction at C**

   iv. Weight of boom   **v. Load at A**

4. Draw the free-body diagram of the (detached) boom showing all these forces labeled with their magnitudes and directions. *Assume* the sense of the vectors representing the *reactions acting on the boom*. Include any other relevant information e.g. lengths, angles etc. which may help when formulating the equilibrium equations (including the moment equation) for the boom.

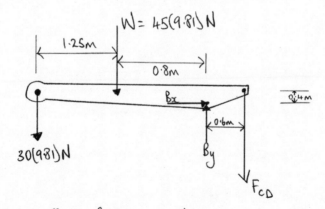

F_{CD} : effect of chain on boom
B_x, B_y : effect of pin on boom
$30(9.81)N$: weight of load (through chain) on boom
W : effect of gravity (weight) on boom

Problem 3.27

Draw a free-body diagram of the beam. Neglect the thickness and weight of the beam.

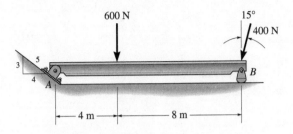

Solution

1. Imagine the beam to be separated or detached from the system.
2. There is a pin connection at A and a rocker support at B. Use Table 2.1 to determine the number and types of reactions *acting on the beam* at A and B.
3. The beam is subjected to five *external* forces. They are caused by:

   i.   ii.

   iii.   iv.

   v.

4. Draw the free-body diagram of the (detached) beam showing all these forces labeled with their magnitudes and directions. *Assume* the sense of the vectors representing the *reactions acting on the beam*. Include any other relevant information e.g. lengths, angles etc. which may help when formulating the equilibrium equations (including the moment equation) for the beam.

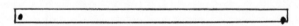

Problem 3.27

Draw a free-body diagram of the beam. Neglect the thickness and weight of the beam.

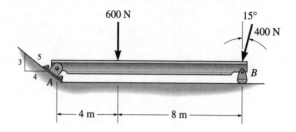

Solution

1. Imagine the beam to be separated or detached from the system.
2. There is a pin connection at A and a rocker support at B. Use Table 2.1 to determine the number and types of reactions *acting on the beam* at A and B.
3. In addition to those shown in the figure, the beam is subjected to three *external* forces. They are caused by:

   i. & ii. The reactions at A   **iii. The reaction at B**

4. Draw the free-body diagram of the (detached) beam showing all these forces labeled with their magnitudes and directions. *Assume* the sense of the vectors representing the *reactions acting on the beam*. Include any other relevant information e.g. lengths, angles etc. which may help when formulating the equilibrium equations (including the moment equation) for the beam.

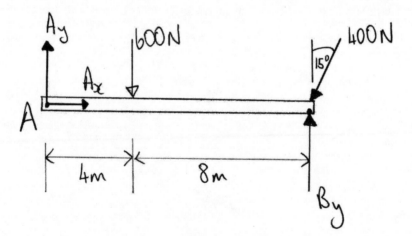

Problem 3.28

The link shown in the figure is pin-connected at A and rests against a smooth support at B. Draw the free-body diagram for link ABC and use it to compute the horizontal and vertical components of reaction at pin A. Neglect the weight of the link.

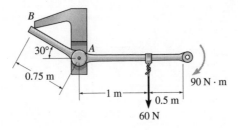

Solution

1. Imagine the link ABC to be separated or detached from the system.
2. There is a pin connection at A and a smooth support at B. Use Table 2.1 to identify the reactions *acting on the link* at A and B.
3. The link is subjected to four *external* forces and one external applied couple moment.
4. Draw the free-body diagram of the (detached) link showing all these forces and couple moments labeled with their magnitudes and directions. *Assume* the sense of the vectors representing the *reactions acting on the link*. Include any other relevant information e.g. lengths, angles etc. which may help when formulating the equilibrium equations (including the moment equation) for the link.

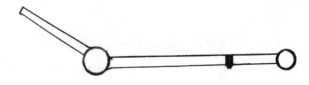

5. Sum moments about A and write down the moment equilibrium equation.

$$\curvearrowright + \sum M_A = 0:$$

6. Establish an xy-axes system on the free-body diagram and write down the force equilibrium equations in each of the x and y-directions

$$\xrightarrow{+} \sum F_x = 0:$$

$$+ \uparrow \sum F_y = 0:$$

7. Solve the three equations for the required reaction components at pin A:

Problem 3.28

The link shown in the figure is pin-connected at A and rests against a smooth support at B. Draw the free-body diagram for link ABC and use it to compute the horizontal and vertical components of reaction at pin A. Neglect the weight of the link.

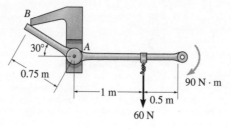

Solution

1. Imagine the link ABC to be separated or detached from the system.
2. There is a pin connection at A and a smooth support at B. Use Table 2.1 to identify the reactions *acting on the link* at A and B.
3. The link is subjected to four *external* forces and one external applied couple moment.
4. Draw the free-body diagram of the (detached) link showing all these forces and couple moments labeled with their magnitudes and directions. *Assume* the sense of the vectors representing the *reactions acting on the link*. Include any other relevant information e.g. lengths, angles etc. which may help when formulating the equilibrium equations (including the moment equation) for the link.

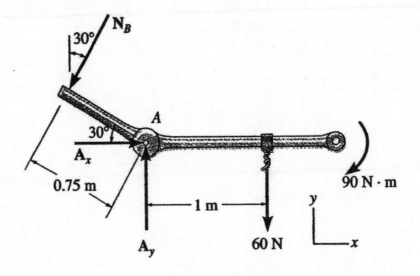

5. Sum moments about A and write down the moment equilibrium equation.

$$\curvearrowleft + \sum M_A = 0: \quad -90N.m - 60N(1m) + N_B(0.75m) = 0$$

6. Establish an xy-axes system on the free-body diagram and write down the force equilibrium equations in each of the x and y-directions

$$\xrightarrow{+} \sum F_x = 0: \quad A_x - N_B \sin 30° N = 0$$

$$+ \uparrow \sum F_y = 0: \quad A_y - N_B \cos 30° N - 60N = 0$$

7. Solve the three equations for the required reaction components at pin A:

$$N_B = 200N, \quad A_x = 100N, \quad A_y = 233N$$ **Ans.**

Problem 3.29

A force of 150 lb acts on the end of the beam. Using the free-body diagram for the beam, find the magnitude and direction of the reaction at pin A and the tension in the cable. Neglect the weight of the beam.

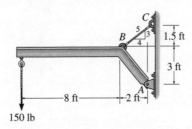

Solution

1. Imagine the beam to be separated or detached from the system.
2. There is a pin connection at A and a cable support at B. Use Table 2.1 to identify the reactions *acting on the beam* at A and B.
3. The beam is subjected to four *external* forces.
4. Draw the free-body diagram of the (detached) beam showing all these forces labeled with their magnitudes and directions. *Assume* the sense of the vectors representing the *reactions acting on the beam.* Include any other relevant information e.g. lengths, angles etc. which may help when formulating the equilibrium equations (including the moment equation) for the beam.

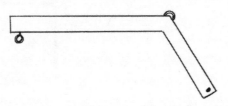

5. Sum moments about A and write down the moment equilibrium equation.

$$\curvearrowleft + \sum M_A = 0:$$

You should obtain the cable tension directly from this equation.

6. Establish an xy-axes system on the free-body diagram and write down the force equilibrium equations in each of the x and y-directions

$$\xrightarrow{+} \sum F_x = 0:$$

$$+ \uparrow \sum F_y = 0:$$

7. Solve the two equations for the magnitude and direction of the (resultant) force at pin A:

Problem 3.29

A force of 150 lb acts on the end of the beam. Using the free-body diagram for the beam, find the magnitude and direction of the reaction at pin A and the tension in the cable. Neglect the weight of the beam.

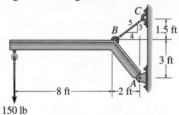

Solution

1. Imagine the beam to be separated or detached from the system.

2. There is a pin connection at A and a cable support at B. Use Table 2.1 to identify the reactions *acting on the beam* at A and B.

3. The beam is subjected to four *external* forces.

4. Draw the free-body diagram of the (detached) beam showing all these forces labeled with their magnitudes and directions. *Assume* the sense of the vectors representing the *reactions acting on the beam*. Include any other relevant information e.g. lengths, angles etc. which may help when formulating the equilibrium equations (including the moment equation) for the beam.

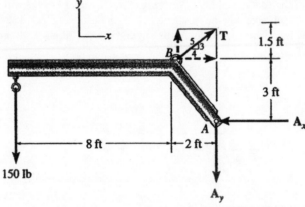

5. Sum moments about A and write down the moment equilibrium equation.

$$\curvearrowleft +\sum M_A = 0: \quad -\left(\frac{3}{5}T\right)(2\text{ ft}) - \left(\frac{4}{5}T\right)(3\text{ ft}) + 150lb(10\,ft) = 0$$

You should obtain the cable tension directly from this equation:

$$T = 416.7 \text{ lb.} \qquad\qquad \textbf{Ans.}$$

6. Establish an xy-axes system on the free-body diagram and write down the force equilibrium equations in each of the x and y-directions

$$\xrightarrow{+} \sum F_x = 0: \quad -A_x + \left(\frac{4}{5}\right)(416.7 \text{ lb}) = 0$$

$$+\uparrow \sum F_y = 0: \quad \left(\frac{3}{5}\right)416.7 \text{ lb} - 150 \text{ lb} - A_y = 0$$

7. Solve the two equations for the magnitude and direction of the (resultant) force at pin A:

$$A_x = 333.3 \text{ lb} \longleftarrow, \quad A_y = 100 \text{ lb} \downarrow$$

Thus, magnitude of force at A is $\sqrt{(333.3)^2 + (100)^2} = 348.0 \text{ lb}$

Direction is $\theta = \tan^{-1}\dfrac{-100}{-333.3} = 196.7°$ 16.7°   **Ans.**

Problem 3.30

The oil-drilling rig shown has a mass of 24 Mg and mass center at G. If the rig is pin-connected at its base, use a free-body diagram of the rig to determine the tension in the hoisting cable and the magnitude of the hoisting force at A when the rig is in the position shown.

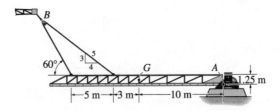

Solution

1. Imagine the rig to be separated or detached from the system.
2. There is a pin connection at A and a cable support at B. Use Table 2.1 to identify the reactions *acting on the rig* at A and B. Note that since the hoisting cable is continuous and passes over the pulley, the cable is subjected to the same tension T throughout its length.
3. The rig is subjected to five *external* forces.
4. Draw the free-body diagram of the (detached) rig showing all these forces labeled with their magnitudes and directions. *Assume* the sense of the vectors representing the *reactions acting on the rig*. Include any other relevant information e.g. lengths, angles etc. which may help when formulating the equilibrium equations (including the moment equation) for the rig.

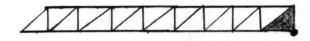

5. Sum moments about A and write down the moment equilibrium equation.

$$\curvearrowleft + \sum M_A = 0:$$

You should obtain the cable tension T directly from this equation:

6. Establish an xy-axes system on the free-body diagram and write down the force equilibrium equations in each of the x and y-directions

$$\underset{\rightarrow}{+} \sum F_x = 0:$$

$$+ \uparrow \sum F_y = 0:$$

7. Solve the two equations for the magnitude of the (resultant) force at pin A:

Problem 3.30

The oil-drilling rig shown has a mass of 24 Mg and mass center at G. If the rig is pin-connected at its base, use a free-body diagram of the rig to determine the tension in the hoisting cable and the magnitude of the hoisting force at A when the rig is in the position shown.

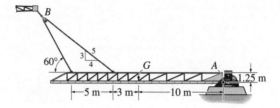

Solution

1. Imagine the rig to be separated or detached from the system.
2. There is a pin connection at A and a cable support at B. Use Table 2.1 to identify the reactions *acting on the rig* at A and B. Note that since the hoisting cable is continuous and passes over the pulley, the cable is subjected to the same tension T throughout its length.
3. The rig is subjected to five *external* forces.
4. Draw the free-body diagram of the (detached) rig showing all these forces labeled with their magnitudes and directions. *Assume* the sense of the vectors representing the *reactions acting on the rig*. Include any other relevant information e.g. lengths, angles etc. which may help when formulating the equilibrium equations (including the moment equation) for the rig.

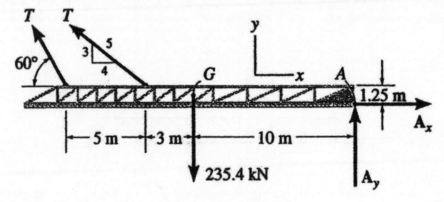

5. Sum moments about A and write down the moment equilibrium equation.

$$\curvearrowleft + \sum M_A = 0: \ (235.4 kN)(10m) - \left(\frac{3}{5}\right)T(13m) + \left(\frac{4}{5}T\right)(1.25m) - T\sin 60°(18m) + (T\cos 60°)(1.25m) = 0$$

You should obtain the cable tension T directly from this equation: $T = 108.2$ kN

6. Establish an xy-axes system on the free-body diagram and write down the force equilibrium equations in each of the x and y-directions

$$\xrightarrow{+} \sum F_x = 0: \ A_x - 108.2\left(\frac{4}{5}\right) \text{ kN} - 108.2\cos 60° \text{ kN} = 0$$

$$+\uparrow \sum F_y = 0: \ A_y - 235.4 \text{ kN} + 108.2\left(\frac{3}{5}\right) \text{ kN} + 108.2\sin 60° \text{ kN} = 0$$

7. Solve the two equations for the magnitude of the (resultant) force at pin A:

$$A_x = 140.6 \text{ kN}, \ A_y = 76.8 \text{ kN}$$

Thus, magnitude of force at A is $\sqrt{(140.6)^2 + (76.8)^2} = 160$ kN   **Ans.**

Problem 3.31

 The forces acting on the plane while it is flying at constant velocity are shown in the figure. If the engine thrust is $F_T = 110$ kip and the plane's weight is $W = 170$ kip, use a free-body diagram to determine the magnitude of the atmospheric drag $\mathbf{F}_D$ and the wing lift $\mathbf{F}_L$. Also determine the distance s to the line of action of the drag force.

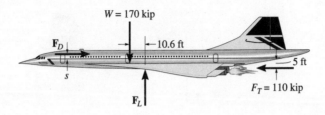

Solution

1. Draw the free-body diagram of the plane showing all external forces labeled with their magnitudes and directions. Include any other relevant information e.g. lengths, angles etc. which may help when formulating the equilibrium equations (including the moment equation) for the plane.

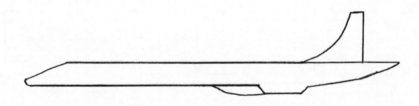

2. Establish an xy-axes system on the free-body diagram and write down the force equilibrium equations in each of the x and y-directions

$$\underset{\rightarrow}{+} \sum F_x = 0:$$

$$+ \uparrow \sum F_y = 0:$$

Each one of these should deliver the magnitudes F_D and F_L directly.

3. Sum moments about a suitable point P and write down the moment equilibrium equation.

$$\curvearrowleft + \sum M_P = 0:$$

With the correct choice of P, you should obtain the distance s directly from this equation.

Problem 3.31

The forces acting on the plane while it is flying at constant velocity are shown in the figure. If the engine thrust is $F_T = 110$ kip and the plane's weight is $W = 170$ kip, use a free-body diagram to determine the magnitude of the atmospheric drag $\mathbf{F}_D$ and the wing lift $\mathbf{F}_L$. Also determine the distance s to the line of action of the drag force.

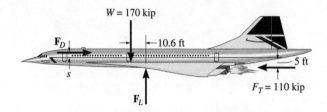

Solution

1. Draw the free-body diagram of the plane showing all external forces labeled with their magnitudes and directions. Include any other relevant information e.g. lengths, angles etc. which may help when formulating the equilibrium equations (including the moment equation) for the plane.

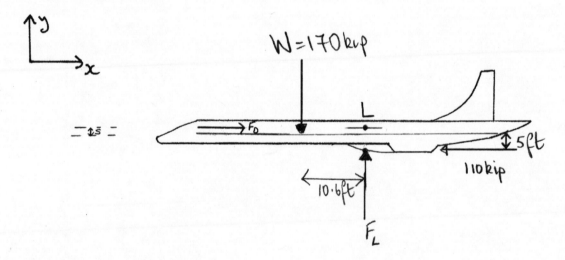

2. Establish an xy-axes system on the free-body diagram and write down the force equilibrium equations in each of the x and y-directions

$$\xrightarrow{+} \sum F_x = 0: \quad F_D - 110 = 0 \Rightarrow F_D = 110 \text{ kip} \qquad \textbf{Ans.}$$

$$+\uparrow \sum F_y = 0: \quad F_L - 170 = 0 \Rightarrow F_L = 170 \text{ kip} \qquad \textbf{Ans.}$$

3. Sum moments about L and write down the moment equilibrium equation.

$$\curvearrowleft +\sum M_L = 0: \quad -110(s + 5) + 170(10.6) = 0 \Rightarrow s = 11.4 \text{ ft} \qquad \textbf{Ans.}$$

Problem 3.32

When holding the 5-lb stone in equilibrium, the humerus H, assumed to be smooth, exerts normal forces $\mathbf{F}_C$ and $\mathbf{F}_A$ on the radius C and ulna A as shown in the figure. Use a free-body diagram to find the magnitude of each of these forces and that of the force $\mathbf{F}_B$ which the biceps B exerts on the radius for equilibrium. The stone has a center of mass at G. Neglect the weight of the arm.

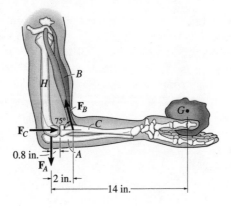

Solution

1. Draw the free-body diagram of the arm and stone together showing all external forces labeled with their magnitudes and directions. Include any other relevant information e.g. lengths, angles etc. which may help when formulating the equilibrium equations (including the moment equation).

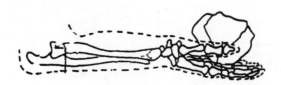

2. Establish an xy-axes system on the free-body diagram and write down the force equilibrium equations in each of the x and y-directions

$$\xrightarrow{+} \sum F_x = 0:$$

$$+\uparrow \sum F_y = 0:$$

3. Sum moments about a suitable point P and write down the moment equilibrium equation.

$$\curvearrowleft + \sum M_P = 0:$$

4. Solve the resulting three equilibrium equations simultaneously for the magnitudes F_A, F_B and F_C:

Problem 3.32

When holding the 5-lb stone in equilibrium, the humerus H, assumed to be smooth, exerts normal forces $\mathbf{F}_C$ and $\mathbf{F}_A$ on the radius C and ulna A as shown in the figure. Use a free-body diagram to find the magnitude of each of these forces and that of the force $\mathbf{F}_B$ which the biceps B exerts on the radius for equilibrium. The stone has a center of mass at G. Neglect the weight of the arm.

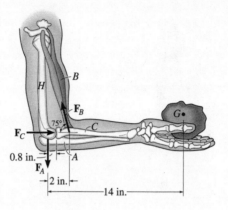

Solution

1. Draw the free-body diagram of the arm and stone together showing all external forces labeled with their magnitudes and directions. Include any other relevant information e.g. lengths, angles etc. which may help when formulating the equilibrium equations (including the moment equation).

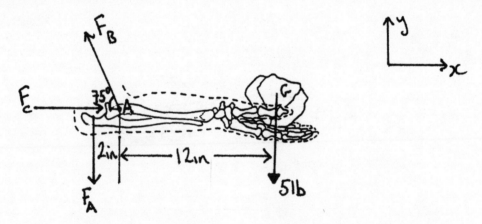

2. Establish an xy-axes system on the free-body diagram and write down the force equilibrium equations in each of the x and y-directions

$$\xrightarrow{+} \sum F_x = 0: \quad F_C - F_B \cos 75° = 0$$

$$+\uparrow \sum F_y = 0: \quad F_B \sin 75° - 5 - F_A = 0$$

3. Sum moments about point A and write down the moment equilibrium equation.

$$\curvearrowright + \sum M_A = 0: \quad -5(12) + F_A(2) = 0$$

4. Solve the resulting three equilibrium equations:

$$F_A = 30 \text{ lb}, \quad F_B = 36.2 \text{ lb} \quad \text{and} \quad F_C = 9.38 \text{ lb}. \qquad \textbf{Ans.}$$

Problem 3.33

Draw a free-body diagram of the beam which is supported by a roller at B, a smooth contact at A and a rocker at C. Neglect the thickness and weight of the beam. Use the free-body diagram to find the magnitude of the reaction where the beam contacts the smooth plane at A.

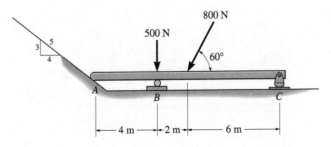

Solution

1. Imagine the beam to be separated or detached from the system.
2. There is a smooth contact at A, a roller at B and a rocker at C. Use Table 2.1 to determine the number and types of reactions *acting on the beam* at A, B and C.
3. The beam is subjected to five *external* forces. They are caused by:

   i.   ii.

   iii.   iv.

   v.

4. Draw the free-body diagram of the (detached) beam showing all these forces labeled with their magnitudes and directions. *Assume* the sense of the vectors representing the *reactions acting on the beam*. Include any other relevant information e.g. lengths, angles etc. which may help when formulating the equilibrium equations (including the moment equation) for the beam.

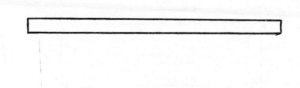

5. Establish an xy-axes system on the free-body diagram and write down the force equilibrium equation in the x-direction

$$\xrightarrow{+} \sum F_x = 0:$$

This is sufficient to deliver directly the magnitude of the reaction at A.

Problem 3.33

Draw a free-body diagram of the beam which is supported by a roller at B, a smooth contact at A and a rocker at C. Neglect the thickness and weight of the beam. Use the free-body diagram to find the magnitude of the reaction where the beam contacts the smooth plane at A.

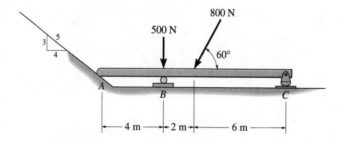

Solution

1. Imagine the beam to be separated or detached from the system.
2. There is a smooth contact at A, a roller at B and a rocker at C. Use Table 2.1 to determine the number and types of reactions *acting on the beam* at A, B and C.
3. The beam is subjected to five *external* forces. They are caused by:

   i. **Reaction at A**   ii. **Reaction at B**

   iii. **Reaction at C**   iv. **500 N load**

   v. **800 N load**

4. Draw the free-body diagram of the (detached) beam showing all these forces labeled with their magnitudes and directions. *Assume* the sense of the vectors representing the *reactions acting on the beam*. Include any other relevant information e.g. lengths, angles etc. which may help when formulating the equilibrium equations (including the moment equation) for the beam.

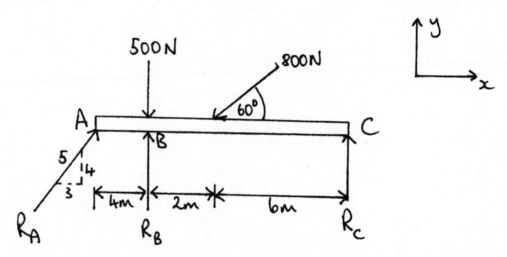

5. Establish an xy-axes system on the free-body diagram and write down the force equilibrium equation in the x-direction

$$+_{\rightarrow} \sum F_x = 0: \quad \left(\frac{3}{5}\right) R_A - 800 \cos 60° = 0$$

This is sufficient to deliver directly the magnitude of the reaction at A i.e. $R_A = 667$ N.   **Ans.**

Problem 3.34

The ramp of a ship has a weight of 200 lb and a center of gravity at G. Draw a free-body diagram for the ramp.

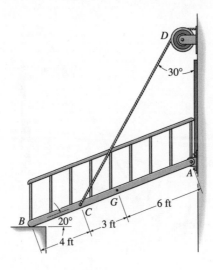

Solution

1. Imagine the ramp to be separated or detached from the system.
2. Use Table 2.1 to determine the number and types of reactions *acting on the ramp* at A, B and C.
3. Draw the free-body diagram of the (detached) ramp showing all the external forces *acting on the ramp* labeled with their magnitudes and directions. *Assume* the sense of the vectors representing the *reactions acting on the ramp*. Include any other relevant information e.g. lengths, angles etc. which may help when formulating the equilibrium equations (including the moment equation) for the ramp.

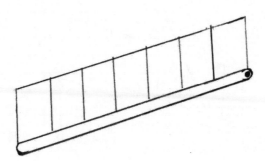

Problem 3.34

The ramp of a ship has a weight of 200 lb and a center of gravity at G. Draw a free-body diagram for the ramp.

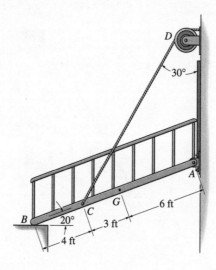

Solution

1. Imagine the ramp to be separated or detached from the system.
2. Use Table 2.1 to determine the number and types of reactions *acting on the ramp* at A, B and C.
3. Draw the free-body diagram of the (detached) ramp showing all the external forces *acting on the ramp* labeled with their magnitudes and directions. *Assume* the sense of the vectors representing the *reactions acting on the ramp*. Include any other relevant information e.g. lengths, angles etc. which may help when formulating the equilibrium equations (including the moment equation) for the ramp.

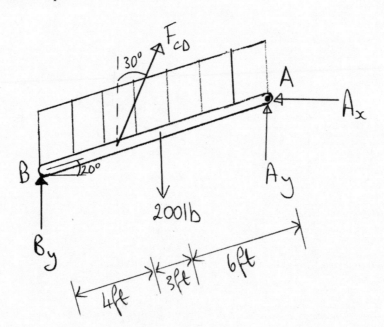

Problem 3.35

The man is pulling a load of 8 lb with one arm held as shown. Draw a free-body diagram of the man's arm and use it to find the magnitude of the force $\mathbf{F}_H$ exerted on the humerus bone H and the magnitude of the tension $\mathbf{T}_B$ developed in the biceps muscle B. Neglect the weight of the arm.

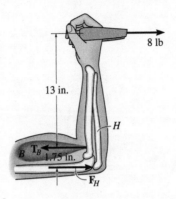

Solution

1. Imagine the arm to be separated or detached from the system.
2. Draw the free-body diagram of the (detached) arm showing all the external forces *acting on the arm* labeled with their magnitudes and directions. Include any other relevant information e.g. lengths, angles etc. which may help when formulating the equilibrium equations (including the moment equation) for the arm.

3. Establish an xy-axes system on the free-body diagram and write down the force equilibrium equation in the x-direction

$$\underset{\rightarrow}{+}\sum F_x = 0:$$

4. Sum moments about B and write down the moment equilibrium equation.

$$\curvearrowleft + \sum M_B = 0:$$

5. Solve the resulting two equilibrium equations (these are sufficient to solve the problem — no need to write down the $y-$equilibrium equation) for the magnitudes F_H and T_B.

Problem 3.35

The man is pulling a load of 8 lb with one arm held as shown. Draw a free-body diagram of the man's arm and use it to find the magnitude of the force $\mathbf{F}_H$ exerted on the humerus bone H and the magnitude of the tension $\mathbf{T}_B$ developed in the biceps muscle B. Neglect the weight of the arm.

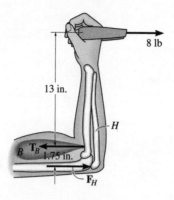

Solution

1. Imagine the arm to be separated or detached from the system.
2. Draw the free-body diagram of the (detached) arm showing all the external forces *acting on the arm* labeled with their magnitudes and directions. Include any other relevant information e.g. lengths, angles etc. which may help when formulating the equilibrium equations (including the moment equation) for the arm.

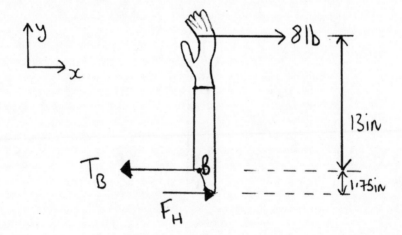

3. Establish an xy-axes system on the free-body diagram and write down the force equilibrium equation in the x-direction

$$\xrightarrow{+} \sum F_x = 0: \quad 8 - T_B + F_H = 0$$

4. Sum moments about B and write down the moment equilibrium equation.

$$\curvearrowleft + \sum M_B = 0: \quad -8(13) + F_H(1.75) = 0$$

5. Solve the resulting two equilibrium equations (these are sufficient to solve the problem — no need to write down the y-equilibrium equation) for the required magnitudes:

$$F_H = 59.4 \text{ lb and } T_B = 67.4 \text{ lb.}$$ **Ans.**

Problem 3.36

Draw a free-body diagram for the beam which is assumed to have negligible weight and thickness. Set $F = 40$ kN and use this information to find the tension in the cord BC.

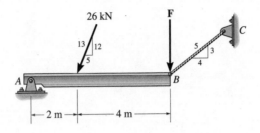

Solution

1. Imagine the beam to be separated or detached from the system.
2. Use Table 2.1 to determine the number and types of reactions *acting on the beam* at A, B and C.
3. Draw the free-body diagram of the (detached) beam showing all the external forces *acting on the ramp* labeled with their magnitudes and directions. *Assume* the sense of the vectors representing the *reactions acting on the beam*. Include any other relevant information e.g. lengths, angles etc. which may help when formulating the equilibrium equations (including the moment equation) for the beam.

4. Sum moments about point A and write down the moment equilibrium equation.

$$\curvearrowleft + \sum M_A = 0:$$

The tension in cord BC should appear directly from this equation.

Problem 3.36

Draw a free-body diagram for the beam which is assumed to have negligible weight and thickness. Set $F = 40$ kN and use this information to find the tension in the cord BC.

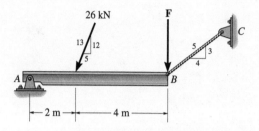

Solution

1. Imagine the beam to be separated or detached from the system.
2. Use Table 2.1 to determine the number and types of reactions *acting on the beam* at A, B and C.
3. Draw the free-body diagram of the (detached) beam showing all the external forces *acting on the ramp* labeled with their magnitudes and directions. *Assume* the sense of the vectors representing the *reactions acting on the beam*. Include any other relevant information e.g. lengths, angles etc. which may help when formulating the equilibrium equations (including the moment equation) for the beam.

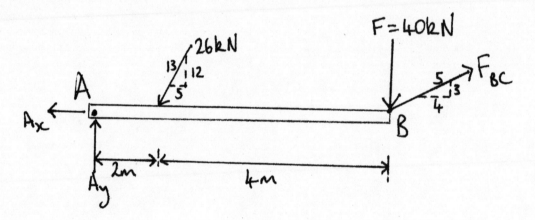

4. Sum moments about point A and write down the moment equilibrium equation.

$$\curvearrowright + \sum M_A = 0: \quad -26\left(\frac{12}{13}\right)(2) - 40(6) + \frac{3}{5}F_{BC}(6) = 0$$

The magnitude of the tension in cord BC is thus $F_{BC} = 80$ kN.   **Ans.**

Problem 3.37

The device is used to hold an elevator door open. There is a pin at *A* and a smooth contact between the roller at *B* and the inclined surface. Draw a free-body diagram for the component *AB*. Neglect the weight of the component.

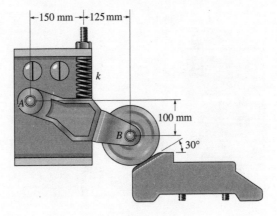

Solution

1. Imagine the member *AB* to be separated or detached from the system.
2. Use Table 2.1 to determine the number and types of reactions *acting on the member* at *A* and *B*.
3. Draw the free-body diagram of the (detached) member showing all the external forces *acting on the member* labeled with their magnitudes and directions. *Assume* the sense of the vectors representing the *reactions acting on the member*. Include any other relevant information e.g. lengths, angles etc. which may help when formulating the equilibrium equations (including the moment equation) for *AB*.

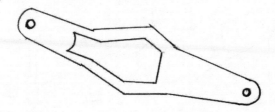

Problem 3.37

The device is used to hold an elevator door open. There is a pin at A and a smooth contact between the roller at B and the inclined surface. Draw a free-body diagram for the component AB. Neglect the weight of the component.

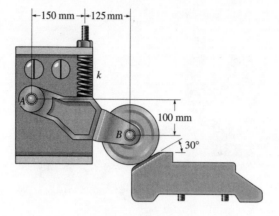

Solution

1. Imagine the member AB to be separated or detached from the system.
2. Use Table 2.1 to determine the number and types of reactions *acting on the member* at A and B.
3. Draw the free-body diagram of the (detached) member showing all the external forces *acting on the member* labeled with their magnitudes and directions. *Assume* the sense of the vectors representing the *reactions acting on the member*. Include any other relevant information e.g. lengths, angles etc. which may help when formulating the equilibrium equations (including the moment equation) for AB.

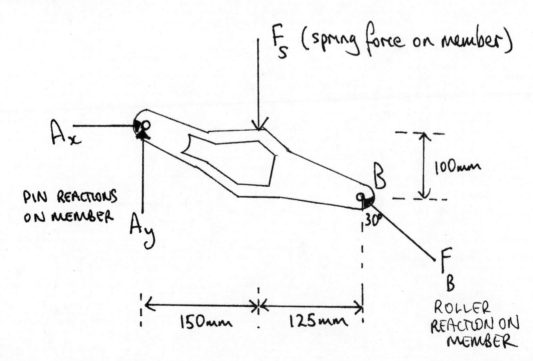

Problem 3.38

The linkage rides along the top and bottom flanges of the crane rail. If the load it supports is 500 lb, use a free-body diagram to determine the magnitude of the force of each roller on the linkage. Neglect the weight of the linkage.

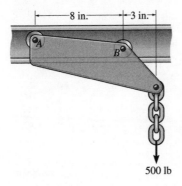

500 lb

Solution

1. Imagine the linkage to be separated or detached from the system.
2. Use Table 2.1 to determine the number and types of reactions *acting on the linkage* at A and B.
3. Draw the free-body diagram of the (detached) linkage showing all the external forces *acting on the linkage* labeled with their magnitudes and directions. *Assume* the sense of the vectors representing the *reactions acting on the linkage*. Include any other relevant information e.g. lengths, angles etc. which may help when formulating the equilibrium equations (including the moment equation).

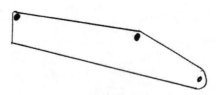

4. Sum moments about point A and write down the moment equilibrium equation.

$$\curvearrowleft + \sum M_A = 0:$$

This should yield directly, the magnitude of the force of the roller at B on the linkage.

5. Establish an xy-axes system on the free-body diagram and write down the force equilibrium equation in the y-direction

$$+\uparrow \sum F_y = 0:$$

This should yield the magnitude of the force of the roller at A on the linkage.

Problem 3.38

The linkage rides along the top and bottom flanges of the crane rail. If the load it supports is 500 lb, use a free-body diagram to determine the magnitude of the force of each roller on the linkage. Neglect the weight of the linkage.

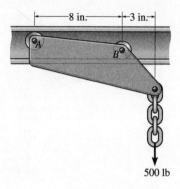

500 lb

Solution

1. Imagine the linkage to be separated or detached from the system.
2. Use Table 2.1 to determine the number and types of reactions *acting on the linkage* at A and B.
3. Draw the free-body diagram of the (detached) linkage showing all the external forces *acting on the linkage* labeled with their magnitudes and directions. *Assume* the sense of the vectors representing the *reactions acting on the linkage*. Include any other relevant information e.g. lengths, angles etc. which may help when formulating the equilibrium equations (including the moment equation).

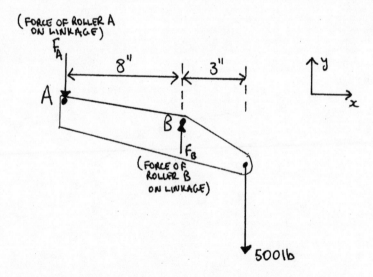

4. Sum moments about point A and write down the moment equilibrium equation.

$$\curvearrowleft + \sum M_A = 0: \quad F_B(8) - 500(11) = 0$$

This yields directly, F_B, the magnitude of the force of the roller at B on the linkage i.e. $F_B = 687.5 \text{ lb}$. **Ans.**

5. Establish an xy-axes system on the free-body diagram and write down the force equilibrium equation in the y-direction

$$+ \uparrow \sum F_y = 0: \quad 687.5 - 500 - F_A = 0$$

This yields the magnitude F_A, of the force of the roller at A on the linkage i.e. $F_A = 187.5 \text{ lb}$. **Ans.**

Problem 3.39

The wall crane is supported by the journal bearing (smooth collar) at B and thrust bearing at A. Draw a free-body diagram for the crane. The thrust bearing at A can support both horizontal and vertical components of force. Neglect the weight of the crane.

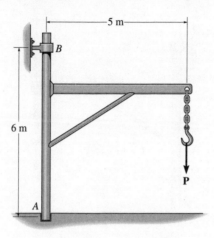

Solution

1. Imagine the crane to be separated or detached from the system.
2. Use Table 2.1 to determine the number and types of reactions *acting on the crane* at A and B.
3. Draw the free-body diagram of the (detached) crane showing all the external forces *acting on the crane* labeled with their magnitudes and directions. *Assume* the sense of the vectors representing the *reactions acting on the crane*. Include any other relevant information e.g. lengths, angles etc. which may help when formulating the equilibrium equations (including the moment equation) for the crane.

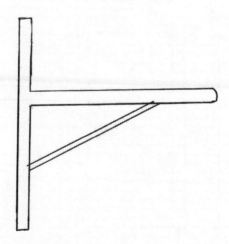

Problem 3.39

The wall crane is supported by the journal bearing (smooth collar) at B and thrust bearing at A. Draw a free-body diagram for the crane. The thrust bearing at A can support both horizontal and vertical components of force. Neglect the weight of the crane.

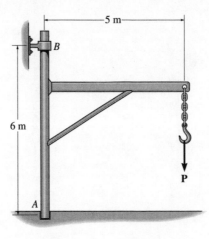

Solution

1. Imagine the crane to be separated or detached from the system.
2. Use Table 2.1 to determine the number and types of reactions *acting on the crane* at A and B.
3. Draw the free-body diagram of the (detached) crane showing all the external forces *acting on the crane* labeled with their magnitudes and directions. *Assume* the sense of the vectors representing the *reactions acting on the crane*. Include any other relevant information e.g. lengths, angles etc. which may help when formulating the equilibrium equations (including the moment equation) for the crane.

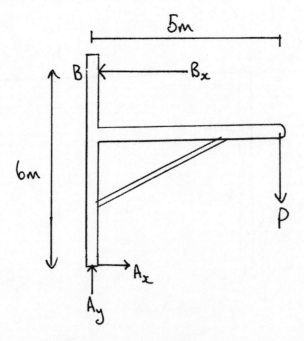

Problem 3.40

The cantilevered jib crane is used to support the load of 780 lb. The trolley T can be placed anywhere between $1.5 \text{ ft} \leq x \leq 7.5 \text{ ft}$. The supports are collars which allow the crane to rotate freely about the vertical axis. The collar at B supports a force in the vertical direction, whereas the one at A does not. Draw a free-body diagram of the crane. Neglect the weight of the crane.

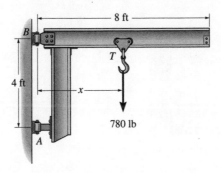

Solution

1. Imagine the crane to be separated or detached from the system.
2. Use Table 2.1 and the information given in the question to determine the number and types of reactions *acting on the crane* at A and B.
3. Draw the free-body diagram of the (detached) crane showing all the external forces *acting on the crane* labeled with their magnitudes and directions. *Assume* the sense of the vectors representing the *reactions acting on the crane*. Include any other relevant information e.g. lengths, angles etc. which may help when formulating the equilibrium equations (including the moment equation) for the crane.

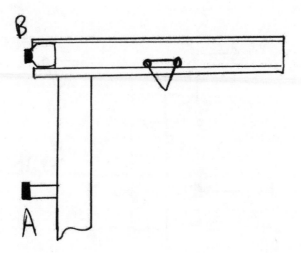

Problem 3.40

The cantilevered jib crane is used to support the load of 780 lb. The trolley T can be placed anywhere between $1.5 \text{ ft} \leq x \leq 7.5 \text{ ft}$. The supports are collars which allow the crane to rotate freely about the vertical axis. The collar at B supports a force in the vertical direction, whereas the one at A does not. Draw a free-body diagram of the crane. Neglect the weight of the crane.

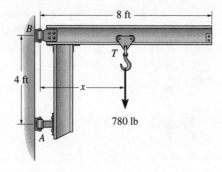

Solution

1. Imagine the crane to be separated or detached from the system.
2. Use Table 2.1 and the information given in the question to determine the number and types of reactions *acting on the crane* at A and B.
3. Draw the free-body diagram of the (detached) crane showing all the external forces *acting on the crane* labeled with their magnitudes and directions. *Assume* the sense of the vectors representing the *reactions acting on the crane*. Include any other relevant information e.g. lengths, angles etc. which may help when formulating the equilibrium equations (including the moment equation) for the crane.

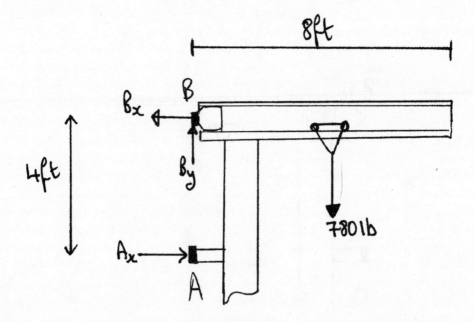

Problem 3.41

The power pole supports the three lines, each line exerting a vertical force on the pole due to its weight as shown. Draw a free-body diagram of the pole. Explain the significance of each force on the diagram. Neglect the weight of the pole.

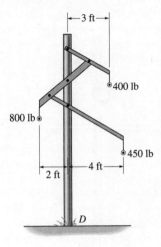

Solution

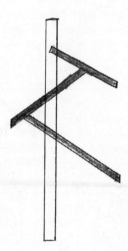

Problem 3.41

The power pole supports the three lines, each line exerting a vertical force on the pole due to its weight as shown. Draw a free-body diagram of the pole. Explain the significance of each force on the diagram. Neglect the weight of the pole.

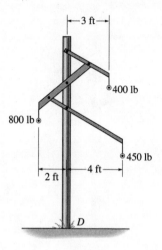

Solution

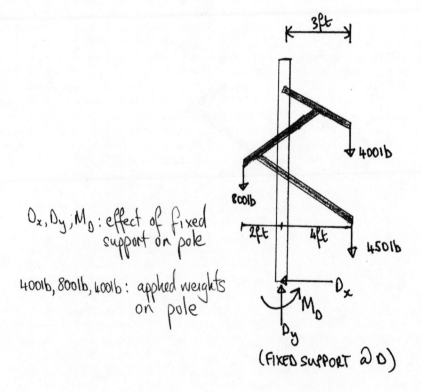

O_x, O_y, M_O : effect of fixed support on pole

400 lb, 800 lb, 400 lb : applied weights on pole

(FIXED SUPPORT @ O)

Problem 3.42

If the wheelbarrow and its contents have a mass of 60 Kg and a center of mass at G, draw a free-body diagram of the wheelbarrow explaining the significance of each force on the diagram. Use this free-body diagram to write down three equilibrium equations. By solving these equations, deduce that the magnitude of the resultant force which the man must exert on *each* of the two handles in order to hold the wheelbarrow in equilibrium is 105.11 N.

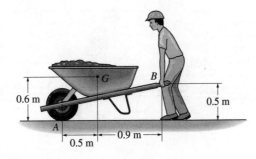

Solution

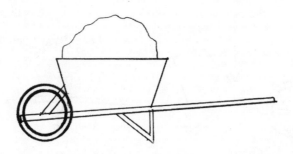

Problem 3.42

If the wheelbarrow and its contents have a mass of 60 Kg and a center of mass at G, draw a free-body diagram of the wheelbarrow explaining the significance of each force on the diagram. Use this free-body diagram to write down three equilibrium equations. By solving these equations, deduce that the magnitude of the resultant force which the man must exert on *each* of the two handles in order to hold the wheelbarrow in equilibrium is 105.11 N.

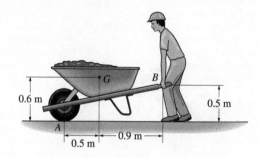

Solution

A_y : effect of surface on wheelbarrow

B_x, B_y : force exerted on each of two handles of wheelbarrow

$60(9.81)N$: weight on wheelbarrow

$60(9.81)N$

$$\curvearrowleft + \sum M_B = 0: \quad -A_y(1.4) + 60(9.81)(0.9) = 0 \Rightarrow A_y = 378.39 \text{ N}$$

$$+\uparrow \sum F_y = 0: \quad 378.39 - 60(9.81) + 2B_y = 0 \Rightarrow B_y = 105.11 \text{ N}$$

$$+_{\rightarrow} \sum F_x = 0: \quad B_x = 0$$

Finally, magnitude of resultant force required is

$$\sqrt{B_x^2 + B_y^2} = 105.11 \text{ N}.$$

Ans.

Problem 3.43

The boom supports the two vertical loads. Neglect the size of the collars at B and D and the thickness and weight of the boom. Set $F_1 = 800$ N and $F_2 = 350$ N. Draw a free-body diagram for the boom. Be sure to label all the force magnitudes and directions explaining the significance of each force on the diagram.

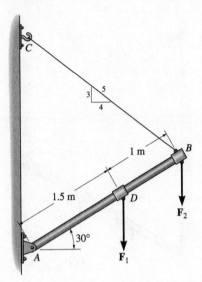

Solution

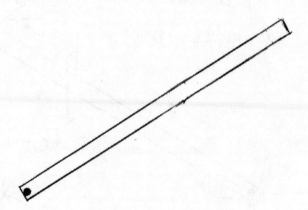

Problem 3.43

The boom supports the two vertical loads. Neglect the size of the collars at B and D and the thickness and weight of the boom. Set $F_1 = 800$ N and $F_2 = 350$ N. Draw a free-body diagram for the boom. Be sure to label all the force magnitudes and directions explaining the significance of each force on the diagram.

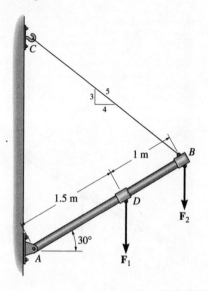

Solution

F_{CB} : effect of cable CB on boom
A_x, A_y : force of pin on boom
F_1, F_2 : effect of weights @ D, B

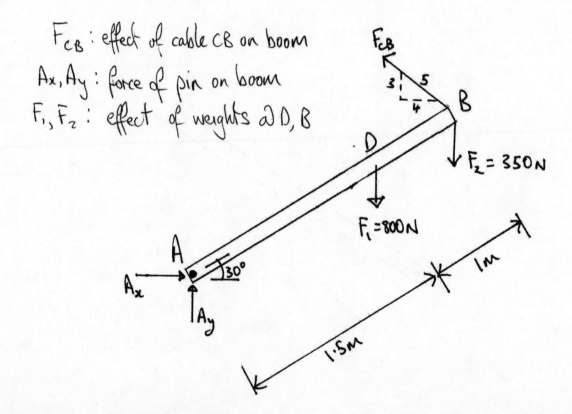

Problem 3.44

Draw a free-body diagram for the linkage ABC. Be sure to label all the force magnitudes and directions explaining the significance of each force on the diagram. The collar at A is smooth. Neglect the weight of each bar.

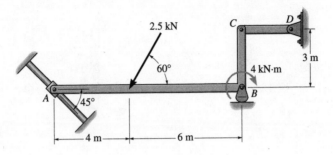

Solution

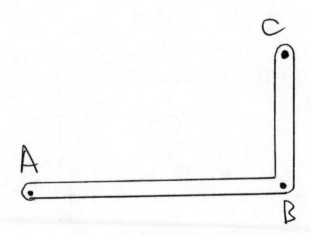

Problem 3.44

Draw a free-body diagram for the linkage ABC. Be sure to label all the force magnitudes and directions explaining the significance of each force on the diagram. The collar at A is smooth. Neglect the weight of each bar.

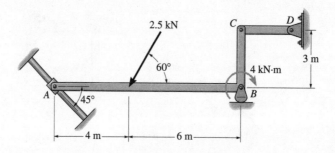

Solution

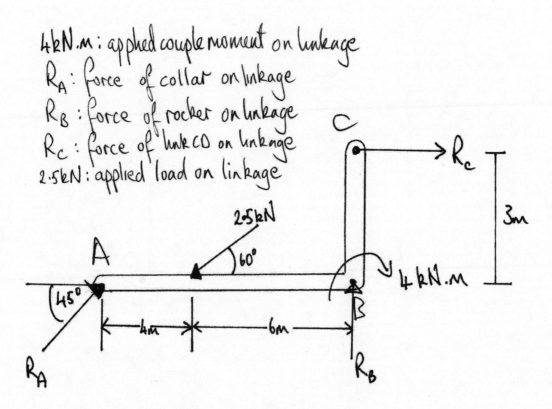

4kN.m : applied couple moment on linkage
R_A : force of collar on linkage
R_B : force of rocker on linkage
R_C : force of link CD on linkage
2.5kN : applied load on linkage

Problem 3.45

The lineman has a weight of 175 lb, mass center at G and stands in the position shown. If he lets go of the pole with his hands, there is a horizontal force on the ring at A and both his feet exert a force on the pole at B. Draw a free-body diagram for the lineman. Be sure to label all the force magnitudes and directions explaining the significance of each force on the diagram. Assume the sides of the belt are parallel.

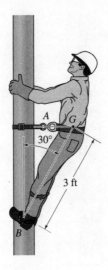

Solution

Problem 3.45

The lineman has a weight of 175 lb, mass center at G and stands in the position shown. If he lets go of the pole with his hands, there is a horizontal force on the ring at A and both his feet exert a force on the pole at B. Draw a free-body diagram for the lineman. Be sure to label all the force magnitudes and directions explaining the significance of each force on the diagram. Assume the sides of the belt are parallel.

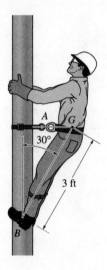

Solution

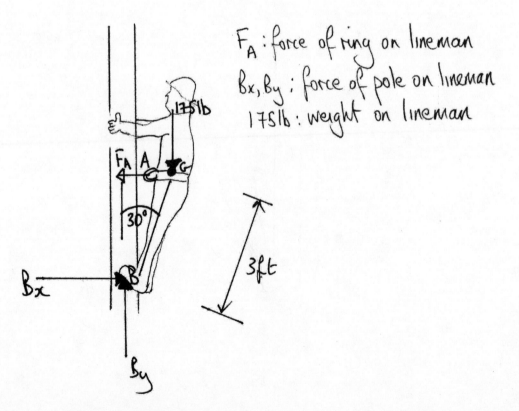

F_A : force of ring on lineman

B_x, B_y : force of pole on lineman

175 lb : weight on lineman

Problem 3.46

The smooth pipe rests against the wall at the points of contact A, B and C. Draw a free-body diagram for the pipe. Be sure to label all the force magnitudes and directions explaining the significance of each force on the diagram. Neglect the thickness and weight of the pipe.

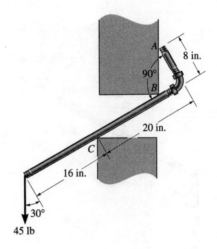

Solution

Problem 3.46

The smooth pipe rests against the wall at the points of contact A, B and C. Draw a free-body diagram for the pipe. Be sure to label all the force magnitudes and directions explaining the significance of each force on the diagram. Neglect the thickness and weight of the pipe.

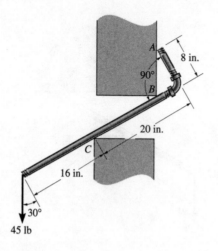

Solution

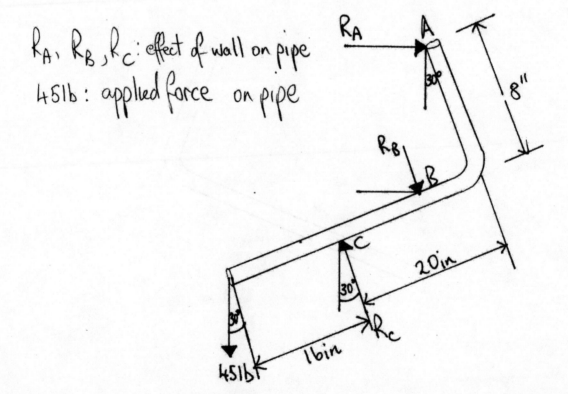

Problem 3.47

The assembly is made from two boards. The board on the left has a weight of 10 lb and center of gravity at G_1 while the board on the right has a weight of 7 lb and a center of gravity at G_2. Draw a free-body diagram of the two boards. Be sure to label all the force magnitudes and directions explaining the significance of each force on the diagram. Include also any other relevant information e.g. lengths, angles etc. which may help when formulating the equilibrium equations (including the moment equation) for the boards.

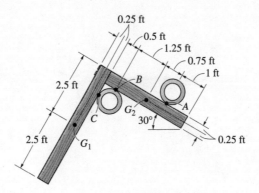

Solution

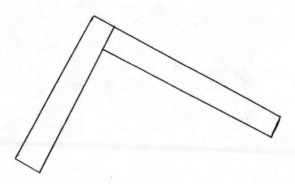

Problem 3.47

The assembly is made from two boards. The board on the left has a weight of $10 lb$ and center of gravity at G_1 while the board on the right has a weight of 7 lb and a center of gravity at G_2. Draw a free-body diagram of the two boards. Be sure to label all the force magnitudes and directions explaining the significance of each force on the diagram. Include also any other relevant information e.g. lengths, angles etc. which may help when formulating the equilibrium equations (including the moment equation) for the boards.

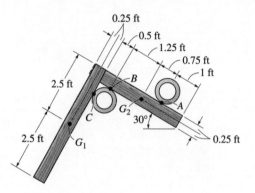

Solution

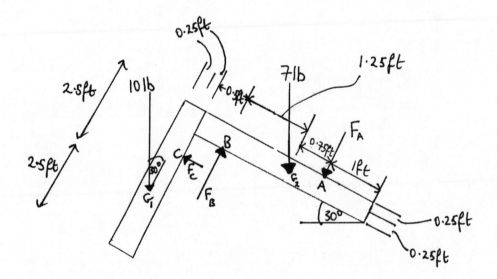

F_A, F_B, F_C : effect of pipes on assembly

$10lb$, $7lb$: weights on assembly

Problem 3.48

The smooth uniform rod has a mass m and is placed on the semicircular arch and against the wall. Draw a free-body diagram of the rod. Be sure to label all the force magnitudes and directions explaining the significance of each force on the diagram. Include also any other relevant information e.g. lengths, angles etc. which may help when formulating the equilibrium equations (including the moment equation) for the rod.

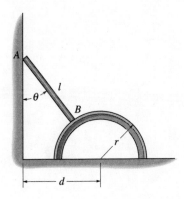

Solution

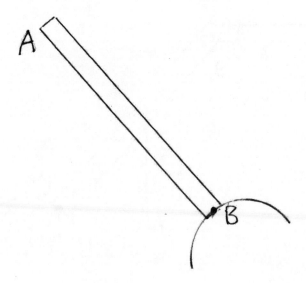

Problem 3.48

The smooth uniform rod has a mass m and is placed on the semicircular arch and against the wall. Draw a free-body diagram of the rod. Be sure to label all the force magnitudes and directions explaining the significance of each force on the diagram. Include also any other relevant information e.g. lengths, angles etc. which may help when formulating the equilibrium equations (including the moment equation) for the rod.

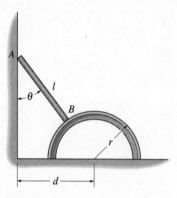

Solution

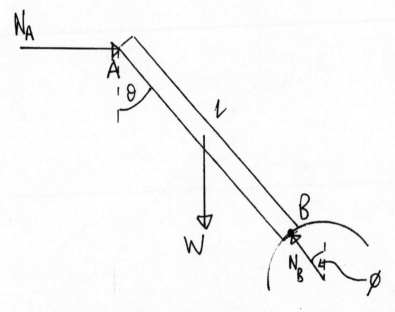

N_A, N_B : effect of surface on rod

W : effect of weight on rod.

Problem 3.49

The uniform ladder has a mass of 60 kg and is placed against the smooth step A. It is lowered to the horizontal position by a man who applies a normal force to it always from a height of 2.5 m. Draw a free-body diagram of the ladder. Be sure to label all the force magnitudes and directions explaining the significance of each force on the diagram. Include also any other relevant information e.g. lengths, angles etc. which may help when formulating the equilibrium equations (including the moment equation) for the ladder.

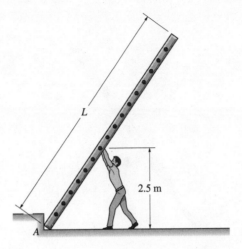

Solution

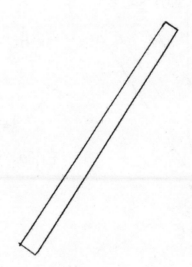

Problem 3.49

The uniform ladder has a mass of 60 kg and is placed against the smooth step A. It is lowered to the horizontal position by a man who applies a normal force to it always from a height of 2.5 m. Draw a free-body diagram of the ladder. Be sure to label all the force magnitudes and directions explaining the significance of each force on the diagram. Include also any other relevant information e.g. lengths, angles etc. which may help when formulating the equilibrium equations (including the moment equation) for the ladder.

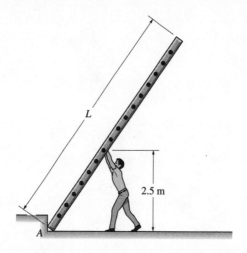

Solution

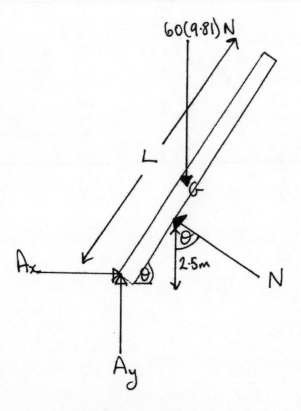

A_x, A_y : effect of surface on ladder

N : normal force applied to ladder

$60(9.81)N$: weight applied to ladder

Problem 3.50

A linear torsional spring deforms in such a way that an applied couple moment M is related to the spring's rotation θ (in radians) by the equation $M = (20\theta)$ N.m. If such a spring is attached to the end of a pin-connected uniform 10 kg rod, using a free-body diagram for the rod, write down the moment equilibrium equation about point A. Deduce the angle θ for equilibrium. The spring is undeformed when $\theta = 0$.

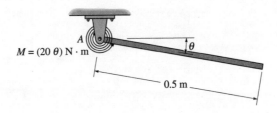

Solution

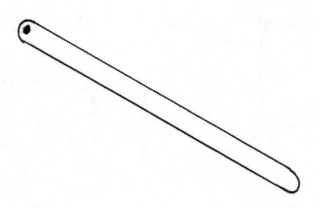

Problem 3.50

A linear torsional spring deforms in such a way that an applied couple moment M is related to the spring's rotation θ (in radians) by the equation $M = (20\theta)$ N.m. If such a spring is attached to the end of a pin-connected uniform 10 kg rod, using a free-body diagram for the rod, write down the moment equilibrium equation about point A. Deduce the angle θ for equilibrium. The spring is undeformed when $\theta = 0$.

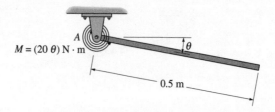

Solution

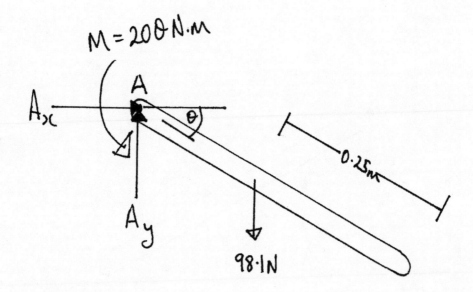

$$\curvearrowleft + \sum M_A = 0: \quad -98.1(0.25\cos\theta) + 20(\theta) = 0$$

Solving for θ: $\theta = 47.5°$ **Ans.**